The C *Revolution*

C000019512

Dr Patrick Dixon

KINGSWAY PUBLICATIONS
EASTBOURNE

ISBN 0 86065 871 6

Produced by Bookprint Creative Services
P.O. Box 827, BN23 6NX, England for
KINGSWAY PUBLICATIONS LTD
Lottbridge Drove, Eastbourne, E Sussex BN23 6NT
Printed in Great Britain by Clays Ltd, St Ives PLC
Typeset by J&L Composition Ltd

THE GENETIC REVOLUTION

Dr Patrick Dixon MA MBBS read medical sciences at King's College Cambridge, completing medical training at Charing Cross Hospital before specialising in the care of the dying and AIDS. He is the founder and medical director of the leading national and international AIDS agency ACET (AIDS Care Education and Training). He is also leader of the Bridge Church in West London and a member of the Pioneer Team. A public speaker and broadcaster, he is author of the highly acclaimed *The Truth About AIDS* and, for a younger readership, *AIDS and You*.

By the same author:
The Truth About AIDS
AIDS and You
HIV: It's Your Choice (booklet)

To Sheila, my wife and best friend

Acknowledgements

I would like to thank Dr Eric Douglas for helping me obtain many of the four hundred references for the book, and the libraries of the Royal Society of Medicine and Charing Cross Hospital whose helpful co-operation saved me many hours in finding information. I am very grateful to Professor R.J. Berry, Professor of Genetics at University College London, who kindly agreed to read early drafts, making numerous helpful comments and clarifying my thinking on a number of technical points. I would also like to thank Dr Alan Johnston, formerly Consultant Physician at Aberdeen Royal Infirmary, for a great number of helpful comments, suggestions and insights into this rapidly changing field. However I take full responsibility for any inaccuracies that remain.

I am indebted to Dr Andrew Fergusson, Secretary of the Christian Medical Fellowship, for his helpful insights and suggestions regarding the chapters on gene ethics, safety, and the gene charter.

I would like to thank Sara Glover and Maggie Chisholm who helped type some of the first draft.

I owe a great deal to Gerald Coates and others of the Pioneer Team for their unfailing support, friendship and encouragement, helping me to understand big issues in the whole context of what God is doing.

Finally my thanks and appreciation are due to Sheila, my wife, and to John, Caroline, Elizabeth and Paul who cheerfully put up with me being busier and less available than usual.

Contents

Introduction

This is a book about a fascinating new revolution. Every day scientists are busy trying to create new animals, plants, bacteria and viruses with the capacity to cure illnesses like AIDS, solve world food shortages and help the environment. Yet the same revolution has the potential to devastate this planet.

The idea for the book arose out of research I did for two earlier books on AIDS, and subsequent work as a doctor in the AIDS field. Back in 1987 it was already clear to me that the next ten years would be revolutionary in terms of being able to reprogram the genetic code of other species, and probably of ourselves. The technology has leapt ahead far faster than I expected, with possibilities regarded as almost science fiction six years ago becoming today's realities.

Decade of the gene

Things are changing so fast that few people are aware of the full impact of what is going on. As we will see, *over 62,000 animals with new genetic code were born in British laboratories in 1991 alone*. The pace is breathtaking. If the 1980s were the decade of the computer microchip, the 1990s have already become the decade of the gene, and by its end every home will contain substances or living organisms resulting from genetic engineering. In 1970 not a single human gene had been isolated; now ten a week are being dissected.[1] We need to understand how it all works, the huge benefits and the very real dangers. We need this technology very badly, as we will see, but with it come major issues which need to be addressed now.

Hundreds of scientific papers have been published on genetic engineering over the last twelve years. I have read the originals or digests of most of these in researching this book over the last two and a half years. The remainder I have also scanned the titles of—being largely of a technical nature and unsuitable for inclusion here. Some readers will be unfamiliar with the science of genetics and will find the first two chapters helpful, while others will want to skip ahead. My purpose is to provide an introduction to the subject so we can then begin to face the issues.

Yesterday's science fiction here today

I have given over 400 notes quoting the relevant scientific papers and press reports, so you can obtain them from a library if more detail is required about the science, politics and ethical issues relating to gene engineering. I have deliberately included quite a few references from the 1980s if only to show how things have developed—some of what you will read about is not as new as you might think. It is hard to believe what is already possible. Indeed, some of the things in this book may sound as though they have been lifted from science fiction. I have attempted to avoid undue speculation, only looking at obvious next steps from progress already made.

There are urgent ethical dilemmas raised by all this. I have left these issues to the end, allowing the facts to present themselves first. I have looked at these questions first as a doctor with a hard-headed practical approach, and secondly as a church leader with a biblical perspective. In researching and writing the book, my own thinking has changed. I deliberately left writing the final chapters until all the research was complete and the major part of the book was written. It has been an exciting, interesting, and at times very alarming journey.

FEBRUARY 1993

I

The End of the Line?

Within ten years life as we know it will have changed significantly —not social, political or cultural life, but the biological nature of life itself. Gene history which has been passed down generations is being dramatically rewritten.

You are the product of your ancestors

The first part of this book has been writ' en in an old Tudor farmhouse built by my ancestors in 1620. John lived here with his wife, eleven children and his parents, but he was not the first to live on the site. His grandfather William was living and working on the same spot around 100 years earlier.

I have a family tree before me which traces the descendants of these few right down as far as the present day. The farmhouse has been lived in or visited by my ancestors throughout the last 400 years. As we sat in front of a blazing log fire in the large living room with its dark oak panelling and beams, we felt echoes from the past. It was easy to imagine what life must have been like so very long ago.

Shaping the next generation

I have often wondered just what else has been passed down over the years. Was it just a memory of stone walls and oak beams? What about inherited family likeness, temperament or personality? Every generation produces a unique blend of two parents, but doubtless some of my 100,000 pieces of inherited information (genes) are even older than John or William themselves.

The words I am writing now (by hand as the word processor is elsewhere) are being scribed on a desk that belonged to my grandfather, also an author of several books (together with an encyclopaedia to his name). Again I have often wondered how much of the compelling drive to write has come from a set of genetic instructions I inherited.

The last generation: mixing genes in babies

For millions of years generations have come and gone: individuals have formed relationships, conceived and brought up children quite literally in the image of themselves. Out of this experience of oneness (however transient) has come a unique historical event: a fusion of their two lives and individuality at the moment of conception to form a brand new mix from them both. Yet for the generation born this year, or next, it could be the end of the line.

The generation being born now may well be the last to have a 'fixed' genetic code, inherited universally in a conventional way. As we will see, there may be few alive in thirty years' time who have not had the genetic code of at least some of their cells reprogrammed away from what they naturally inherited. To some extent this has already been happening as a result of radiation induced mutations. Some may acquire genetic changes which will outlast their own lives because they will be passed on to their children, their grandchildren and their great-grandchildren. Subsequent generations will have to judge whether this is a blessing or a biological curse.

From bacteria to humans

The quite extraordinary thing about the code of life is that it is so constant. The smallest most primitive living organism has a book of life written in exactly the same language and structured in an identical way to the largest creature in existence. For evolutionists this comes as no surprise; neither does it to those who believe the sense of the Genesis account is true (not necessarily literal timings or order) and that when God spoke, his language of creation was written in the universal language of life known today as genetic code contained in genes.

Genes from bacteria work in humans, human genes work in monkeys, and monkey genes work in viruses. In the test-tube of the laboratory and in the brain of the desktop computer a revolution is taking place in front of our eyes, yet few realise what is happening or understand the consequences.

New humans, cows, tomatoes and cures

For centuries, people have dreamed of being able to stop themselves growing old,[2] of altering themselves, or each other, or of being able to produce 'clones'. More recently, parents have thought not only of choosing the sex of their children, but also of being able to influence the development of their children to produce high intelligence, attractive personality, healthy constitution, athletic body, musical ability—and maybe even an obedient nature.[3]

Farmers have dreamed of low-fat cows, non-bruised tomatoes, cold-resistant bananas, corn which comes up year after year without seeding, and other strange creations. Parents of children with inherited diseases such as cystic fibrosis, where the lung problems are a result of faulty genetic code, have dreamed of a day when doctors might be able to program the faulty gene back.[4]

Those with AIDS have dreamed of a cure for HIV infection, reversing the damage done to cells by the virus called HIV, which programs white cells to produce more viruses instead of fighting infection.

To say that all these things are already possible would be a gross exaggeration. However, as we shall see, the machinery and most of the knowledge are already here. But before we look at what is happening now we need to see the gene revolution in an historical context.

Discovery leads revolution

Man's greatest discoveries have often happened by accident or curiosity, yet have started social revolutions. It was by accident that ancient man found metal in the fire after heating earth, and glass after heating sand. The first steam engines in 1698 led to a massive demand for coal and the rapid industrialisation of England.[5]

Then came the discovery of electricity in 1820 and the means of storing it in a battery in 1836, together with the means of generating it using magnets and massive coils of wire turning at high speed by 1850, with industrial power generation by 1880.

The petrol engine invented in 1885 has had a massive impact continuing today. Radio transmission started in 1901 as yet another curious experiment before leading to television in 1936 and today's satellite technology.

Often the work of the inventor is hijacked by urgent need. The Second World War accelerated work on penicillin, aircraft engines, rockets, radar and nuclear energy. The continued arms race in the cold war of the 1950s and 1960s, together with the American space programme goal to walk on the moon, led to a massive search for ways to reduce the weight of electronic equipment. Glass valves used a lot of heat, took time to warm up, were unreliable and heavy. A rocket full of glass was unlikely to go far.

Lessons from microchips

Then the age of the silicon transistor dawned. By the 1960s transistor radios were proudly displayed in every High Street, priced according to the number of transistors they contained. Within a few years, scientists had found ways to produce millions of transistors on one small sheet the size of a coin. A huge computer occupying a massive air-conditioned room could now be compressed into a metal box inside a briefcase, running on batteries.

In 1980 people were predicting that in ten years every person in the country would own things containing these 'silicon chips'—in cars, washing machines, radios, electric mixers or calculators, to name but a few. At the time this looked a little far-fetched, but by 1988 it was already a reality. By the mid-1980s most shops had converted to electronic cash registers, most banks were using electronic cash dispensers and transistor radios were in junk shops.

Most of these discoveries were made by inventive, curious people searching for answers to particular problems. Few realised at the time how revolutionary their discoveries would be. As we shall see, the same is true of genetic engineering today.

Lightning change

Every ten years, our total scientific knowledge is doubling: we knew twice as much about the world in 1950 than in 1940, four times as much by 1960, eight times as much by 1970, sixteen times as much by 1980 and by 1990, we knew over thirty times as much scientifically as fifty years previously. By the year 2000, we will know sixty to one hundred times as much as we did then.

The pace of discovery is increasing so fast that human brains cannot understand it all. We are already facing major problems with complex equipment such as computers, because there is not one brain in the world capable of understanding the whole machine. When unexpected things happen, it can be extremely difficult to understand why, and how to solve the problem.

Chips today—redundant tomorrow

Even if no new progress is made in computer design for the rest of this century, it will take programmers at least another ten years from now to get to grips with what today's machines are really capable of.

I am emphasising these points because unless we understand what is happening in electronics now, we will not fully understand the impact of new genes in the future, where once again the tools and equipment available are developing enormously faster than our thinking about how to use them. However, there is one big difference: computers may make people redundant in many jobs, but they do not alter life itself. Genetic engineering, on the other hand, by definition alters the very substance on which life is based.

The gene revolution

So, into this new computerised age, we now add the age of the gene, with greater potential to help than the microchip, and as we shall see (if the technology is used unwisely for peaceful or military purposes) a greater power to harm than a dozen nuclear reactors or atomic bombs.

The gene revolution is being developed under exactly the same pressures as the micro-revolution or any other of the major discoveries this century: driven by curiosity and commercial interest built on urgent human need.

Pleasure today, but future nightmare

As we approach the third millennium, we are faced with a series of nightmares that are so hellish that most of us manage to avoid thinking about them. Global warming is not one of them.

My eldest son, John, who is ten, has a freshness in his view of the world. Every week his eyes of understanding open wider and his insights become sharper. Many growing problems are already obvious to him—and also to genetic engineers.

1. Energy shortage

He knows that within his lifetime, the one-third affluent world will largely have burned out all the main sources of oil and gas. Coal will remain, but will be scarce and expensive. How are we going to keep warm or powered up in tomorrow's world—not just for the next sixty years, but for the next 2,000 years? We are acting as if there is no tomorrow, no future, no subsequent generations to worry about.

The world population is growing faster than ever, and many two-thirds world cities are mushrooming chaotically in size and problems. By the year 2000 the great majority of the world's growing population will be living in towns or cities. A new wave of industrialisation must follow to improve standards of living and provide jobs for the millions of new city-dwellers.

2. Materials shortage

Industry uses power, iron ore, aluminium, copper, oil, stone, wood, gold, silver, diamonds. The resources will run out faster. Scarcer resources carried further at greater cost will create further hyper-inflation in many countries, and possibly bankruptcy for some of the most vulnerable.

3. Oxygen shortage

Then there is the problem of food—or rather also the problem of oxygen. Global warming happens when the carbon dioxide we breathe out, also released by burning fuels, rises in the atmosphere trapping the heat of the sun. Carbon dioxide rises as oxygen falls.

When the sun is shining, plants and trees use the energy to build fibre or wood out of carbon dioxide gas, releasing precious oxygen back into the atmosphere. Trees are cut down for fuel, for building materials, or to clear land for growing food. With clearance of forests, how will tomorrow's world be supplied with oxygen?

4. Massive epidemics

There is another problem where the population or cities have grown fast: epidemics of disease, or plagues. By the mid-1980s there was hardly a country in the world not hit by a new worldwide plague, spreading faster than scientists had techniques to monitor it. Known as the silent killer, it had the capacity to destroy for some ten to twenty years before the devastating effects were fully seen. I am, of course, referring to the disease AIDS. The causative agent HIV has already infected thirteen million people worldwide.

The death toll from AIDS in the United States alone has already exceeded double that of the Vietnam War, with a total of almost a million infected and likely to need care in the future. In Africa I have recently visited countries where a silent holocaust has already taken place among the young, with a million deaths already, of which a great number have been children or babies infected through the womb. In some areas one adult in three is already infected. At least one country is giving reliable test survey figures showing average infection levels as high as one adult in six throughout the entire population, including the most inaccessible rural areas.[6]

AIDS is a late-twentieth-century problem: it is mainly a heterosexually spread disease worldwide (over 75% of total world infections currently, expected to rise soon to 90% of total). The rapid spread of HIV is part of a massive global epidemic of a number of other sexually-transmitted diseases, related to an increase in the number of sexual partners per average adult in the course of a lifetime. This has been accompanied by a huge increase in mobility enabling millions to move from town to town or from continent to continent each year. Syphilis was also known as a plague in previous centuries. Until the 1940s there was no cure. It killed after ten to twenty years, it was spread sexually and children could be infected at birth.

These are just a few of the problems my own children will be confronted with. Progress measured by the microchip, the petrol engine, the discovery of antibiotics, burning earth to make steel, burning coal to make power—none of these society-changing discoveries brings any answers. In fact, these discoveries have simply added to the growing number of problems of increasing consumption and increasing population as general health improves and child mortality falls.

So what can the gene revolution contribute to such a world? Redesigned organisms could offer us new ways to convert scarce sources of energy, including coal and industrial wastes, to substances we can use to make recyclable plastics. New organisms could provide new food sources, while new ultra-efficient plants and faster growing trees could be part of the world lungs of the future. Finally, altered microbes could offer complete cures for diseases such as AIDS and malaria.

The challenge is there—and it looks like genetic engineering may be the best way to meet that challenge. At what cost, we will see as we look further into this exciting, alarming world of experiment and discovery.

However, before we can swop genes from one species to another, we need to understand how cells work and why such changes produce dramatic results. The story starts in an Austrian monastery in 1860 with a monk who, some might say, was playing God.

2

Playing God

The most remarkable thing about life on earth is how constant it is. From the most ancient times until now insects have bred insects, birds bred birds, cows bred cows and humans given birth to humans. If you take acorns from an oak tree and plant them, you expect more oak trees. Creatures and plants remain true to type, faithfully passing on their characteristics from generation to generation. Wherever there are slight variations, for example in skin pigmentation or in the colouring of flowers, then these too can usually be traced down the generations. Considering its complexity, life has been very stable. The process by which this inheritance came about was not understood however.

I am going to explain how life works as simply as I can, assuming you have no specialist knowledge, so you can then understand what scientists are doing to alter life. Some of this is a little complicated—just skip over sections you don't understand, because by the end it will be much clearer. (If you are an expert in the field, you may want to jump ahead to around page 43 or to the beginning of the next chapter.)

The cell structure of living organisms was only discovered by Robert Hooke in 1663, and the idea that all organisms were built up from identical cells was only proposed in 1839. It was almost a hundred years later before we began to understand how cells work. Most of the structures in a cell could only be seen with the high power of the electron microscope invented in 1933.[7] However, many centuries ago breeding experiments were already taking place—the earliest technique of genetic engineering.

A curious Austrian monk

In around 1860 an Austrian monk called George Mendel was working in the potting sheds of his monastery. He was curious to know what would happen if he took pollen from one type of plant and used it to fertilise another. Would the pollen be accepted? Would it fertilise the plant? Would the seeds germinate, and what kind of plant would grow?

For thousands of years previously farmers had cross-bred animals. For instance, in the time of Jesus, it was common to allow horses to mate with donkeys: the result was a rather strange-looking creature at birth known as a mule. This new species had one important drawback: you could not breed from it because it was always sterile.

Hundreds of other examples could be given over previous centuries of selective breeding—indeed Jacob in the Old Testament seemed to know what he was doing in selectively breeding white and black sheep to produce a herd entirely coloured as he wanted, at a time when sheep ownership was being determined solely by the colouring of their woollen coats.

The process of inheritance has been well understood by families who observe, say, grandpa's red hair passed on to a grandchild, or other family likenesses. However, the mechanism has only relatively recently been fully understood. Why do dark-haired parents occasionally produce a fair-haired child?

Designing new plants

Mendel was interested in all of this. Moreover, the monastery stood to gain from improved strains of cereal plants. Mendel found that when he cross-fertilised closely related plants with obvious differences, he got neither a mix nor equal numbers of each type. Instead he found a curious pattern. After a while he could predict in advance not only what variations he would see, but also how many of them. He realised that each seed contained more information than would ever be used to form the new plant.

Much of this information was hidden away in many plants and only expressed when cross-fertilisation took place. Each plant seemed to have its own strong (dominant) and weak (recessive) features. Weak features only came to the surface under certain circumstances.

Hidden genes

Similar understanding is used daily in dozens of genetic engineering laboratories all over the world. When Mendel cross-fertilised tall and short varieties of the same plants, he found he always landed up with new plants in a fixed ratio of three tall to one short. From this he proposed a theory which was to revolutionise our thinking about breeding.[8]

He came to the conclusion that each plant must have two sets of instructions for each part of its makeup, including height. If the plant had mixed instructions, then one set would dominate—in this instance the instructions for increased height—while the other set remained hidden.

Sperm and egg genes fight for power

You can see how this works in Fig 1. When sperms or eggs are made—or their equivalent in plants—the original cells divide into two, with only half the set of instructions needed for life in each. So parents with a mixture of tall and short instructions in their cells will produce sperm or eggs with either one or the other.

Fertilisation happens in plants when pollen and ova meet (their equivalent of sperm and eggs in animals). When pollen and ova fuse together at fertilisation, the new composite cell inherits a complete set of instructions and is able to start forming a new plant. Clearly four types of plants could result: one type where pollen and ova have both provided tall instructions, another where both are short, and two where there is a mix. Three out of four will be tall. The only short plant will be one where both sets of instructions are short, because both parent plants passed on the recessive trait.

Fig 1

'Mother'   'Father'

T S   T S

Both these plants have a tall gene in the pair, so both are tall.

Fig 2

1. Mother   Father
        T   T   A tall plant

2. Mother   Father
        T   S   A tall plant

3. Mother   Father
        S   T   A tall plant

4. Mother   Father
        S   S   A short plant

So in Mendel's classic experiment, two tall plants produced short plants one time in four. Interestingly, if short plants are only fertilised by other short plants, you can see that no more tall plants will ever be produced. A new strain will emerge.

Pedigree dogs weakened for life

Simple methods like this have been widely used by gardeners and horticulturists for over a hundred years: breeding selectively from plants showing the best characteristics. The development of pedigree dogs is an ancient art which works on the same principle: only allowing dogs that have the right features to mate.

However, breeders are hit by a major problem: if they go on interbreeding from just one small group, then more and more weak recessive genes may emerge. Some may have hidden dangers for the animal. Take dogs again as an example: in the wild they breed widely, producing a group of fairly even appearance with mixed genetic code. If weak traits emerge, they tend to be eliminated because those dogs do not survive long enough to breed, or because the recessive traits are covered up by dominant genes from others in the group.

However, domestic breeding deliberately trims out dominant genes. The result may be a beautiful breed, but one which is susceptible to a high rate of blindness, tumours or hip problems for example.

Pedigree humans and disease

There are many inherited disorders in humans that can arise in a similar way. In these so-called 'autosomal recessive' illnesses, the parents are usually completely healthy but silent carriers of the same weak gene. Since related individuals are more likely to be carrying a copy of the same gene, when cousins marry, the children are more likely to inherit two copies of the weak gene, so the recessive gene will express itself. Examples of such weak genes are those causing albinism, phenylketonuria and cystic fibrosis. A great number of illnesses have more complex causes, with several genes contributing to the likelihood of disease together with environmental influences. Such conditions are known as multi-factorial and include, as we shall see later, heart disease, high blood pressure and cancer.

The result then of human interbreeding is a 'pedigree' with problems similar to overbred animals. There is then a biological basis for the biblical injunction against close relatives inter-marrying. Cross-fertilisation is needed to keep us all healthy.

The Royal Disease

Haemophilia is a disease where blood does not clot properly so people can bleed to death in severe cases. In the last century haemophilia was known as the Royal Disease because it was common in the European Royal Family. The gene causing the problem is recessive and sex-linked, so women are carriers and men have the disease. We will see why later.

In those with haemophilia the missing substance is called Factor 8—a substance found in normal blood and one component of the clotting mechanism. Factor 8 can be extracted from blood donated for blood transfusion, although the process is complicated and expensive. If someone with haemophilia is bleeding uncontrollably from a cut or internal injury, an injection of Factor 8 stops it very effectively.

AIDS danger came from blood

The extraction process has turned out to be very unsafe, however. The virus causing AIDS found its way into donated blood in many different parts of the world. Whereas an infected blood transfusion to an uninfected person only results in one new infection, Factor 8 is obtained by pooling plasma from a number of different people.

Just one donation in a hundred can be enough to contaminate the whole process so that dozens become infected. Effective testing from 1985 (using techniques derived from genetic engineering) has almost eliminated this risk in many countries. However, testing came too late for over 1,000 men and 250 boys already infected by then in the UK alone.

Pressure has been growing to make Factor 8 in the laboratory as an alternative to using blood. In 1984 the genes programming for Factor 8 were identified, copied and analysed.[9] In the last two to three years genetic engineering has been used to program cells from mammals grown in the laboratory or factory to produce human Factor 8.[10] We will be looking at this remarkable achievement in more detail later on.

Haemophilia for men only

Mendel's experiments show us why all those with haemophilia are men. The interesting thing about haemophilia is that the gene carrying information on blood clotting just happens to be sitting on the X or female chromosome. This 'linkage' of one characteristic (sex) with another (clotting) is extremely important to the genetic engineer, as we shall see later on. Linkage with an outward obvious sign is a good marker of other genes also inherited in the 'package'.

All the genes or sets of instructions in a human are contained in just forty-six chromosomes, each of which exists as one of twenty-two pairs, together with the sex chromosomes. Chromosomes can be seen under the microscope and most look quite similar. However, there is an obvious difference between men and women: women have a pair of chromosomes shaped like two Xs, while men have one X chromosome and another shaped like a Y. The Y is always active and has a profound effect on the embryo, so a single Y produces a boy. The haemophilia defect is on the X chromosome, so women never get the disease because the other X chromosome has enough information on it to prevent clotting problems, although they can be carriers.

How same genes make different cells

So now we understand what genes are and how they are inherited, we can begin to see how and why scientists are swopping or modifying them, making artificial chromosomes (strings of genes).[11] There is one further thing we need to understand. While almost every human cell contains a full set of chromosomes with all the genes for the whole person, each cell uses only a minute fraction of the information.[12]

One of the greatest puzzles in medicine is how, for example, a kidney cell knows it is a kidney cell and not a piece of skin. The chromosomes are the same, the genes are the same, the full genetic code is the same. Yet each cell type is only using part of the full set of instructions.

We need first to understand how cells work: each cell in the body has a similar structure not very different from the cells of every other living creature. Cells are tiny. Around a million will just about cover a square measuring one centimetre by one centimetre. Each of these cells is basically a miniature chemical factory with three parts: a brain (nucleus), cell fluid (cytoplasm) and a cell wall to keep it all together.

Cell wall

All cells are like tiny balloons or bags. The bag itself is made of a special membrane which functions like a factory wall: it keeps things in and others out. There are gates in the wall which open or close at various times to take in food or dispose of manufactured goods.

There are also pumps in the wall which push substances in or out. These pumps are like factory air-conditioning units, keeping the internal environment constant whatever is happening outside. The water inside may need to be kept saltier for example, or there may even be a need for there to be an electrical charge stored inside the cell like a tiny battery. This means electric current can flow when the cell wall gates are suddenly opened, for example to allow nerve cells to conduct electrical impulses.

If cell walls are exposed to various chemicals they become leaky, not only allowing unusual substances out, but also allowing all kinds of things to drift inside the cell from surrounding fluid. This is very important for the genetic engineer. As we shall see later, a favourite trick is to place cells in a liquid containing fragments of genetic code, and make the cells leaky so the fragments move inside.

Nucleus

Inside the cell there is a bag within a bag. This second bag is much smaller, but has a similar function. This bag keeps all the chromosomes together inside the cell. Every instruction the cell needs is in the nucleus. The nucleus is the equivalent of the cell brain, or the factory management office.

Cytoplasm

Outside the nucleus, the rest of the cell is far from empty: the space is stuffed full of a maze of corridors or tubing, called endoplasmic reticulum, as well as factory assembly units called ribosomes, and power supply units called mitochondria.

Since chromosomes and their genes never leave the cell nucleus, how do the ribosome units know what to make and when? There is a special communication system which takes messages from the inside of the nucleus to the ribosome assembly lines. It works on the same principle as a fax machine or a photocopier and courier service. These very same principles are used by genetic engineers all the time to copy instructions. But first we need to understand a little more about how a chromosome stores its vital information.

The ultimate information and production unit

Every human contains five billion of these cells, each containing more information than most laptop computers, yet also capable of producing more complex structures than huge laboratories. These biological factories are the ultimate in miniaturisation. In the human body these cells operate as a community, constantly communicating with each other through hormones and other chemical messengers.

How to read your genes

If you take a chromosome apart into its tens of thousands of genes, and take each gene apart one by one, you will find each one is made up of a long string of building blocks or molecules. There are around 3,000,000,000 of these used in every human cell.[13] When they are strung together they are called nucleic acids, because they are chemically slightly acidic and they are used in the nucleus of a cell. The nucleic acids themselves are called DNA (or deoxyribonucleic acid). DNA is built up of only four different building blocks known as bases.[14]

These create a special four-letter 'alphabet' formed from the different shapes of the four structures: Adenine, Thymine, Guanine and Cytosine, or A, T, G and C for short. Assembled DNA consists of two strands that look a little like a model railway track. Each rail is a long string of the four bases in a special language sequence—ATGCCTA for example. These chemicals operate in reverse pairs so that if, say, A is one side of the track, T is always on the other; G always pairs with C and the other way round is also true. The pairs are joined together like the sleepers of a railway track (see Fig 3).

Fig 3: Building blocks or bases forming nucleic acid (DNA)

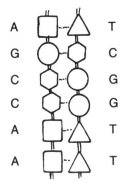

There is one other important feature: when the double track is formed, it has a natural coil to it so it circles round and round like a spring. This spring shape is called a double helix (Fig 4). This coiled structure was first discovered by James Watson and Francis Crick in 1953, winning a Nobel Prize in 1962. The 3,000,000,000 pairs of bases are held in groups of 100,000 genes.

Fig 4: The coiling that happens with DNA once made

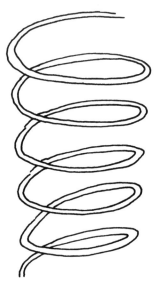

'*Encyclopaedia Britannica*' in every cell

When a gene is dismantled, you can write out the order of bases as a code or language—even with punctuation marks and start/stop instructions. Typing out the full language from all your own genes would fill more than the *Encyclopaedia Britannica*. A lot of information is repeated twice and many pages are 'spare'—filled with a jumble of words and phrases apparently not being used at all.

Each cell in your body contains the full encyclopedia, but only uses a few pages.[15] All the other genes are 'turned off' or deactivated. To put it another way, the other volumes of the encyclopedia are in the bookshelf unopened. One feature of cancer cells is that the wrong volume of the encyclopedia is open: the wrong genes are activated, sending accurate but inappropriate instructions to cells to grow and usually to become less specialised.

How genes control your cells

So how exactly are these instructions sent? The cell uses a second form of genetic code called RNA (or ribonucleic acid) to make a precise copy of DNA. The RNA is also written in a four-letter code, the only difference being that it uses Uracil or U instead of Thymine or T. Once this messenger RNA has been printed off, it passes through the wall of the nucleus and is carried through the cytoplasm until it reaches a ribosome factory. And then the real action begins.

Every protein structure in the human body is built out of twenty differently shaped building blocks called amino acids. The body finds it very difficult to make amino acids, which is why we need them in our diet—obtained from protein in meat, vegetables or other plant sources. Protein is broken down in the gut to amino acids which are then absorbed.

Playing with building blocks

There is almost no limit to the shapes that can be built with these chains of amino acids (otherwise known as polypeptides). As the chains are assembled piece by piece, they start to bend and kink, with curves and straight sections appearing in different places according to which different building blocks are where.

As the folding up continues, building blocks which were in the centre of the long string can find that they are almost touching building blocks near the beginning or at the end. Some building blocks tend to pull towards each other as if magnetised, and these 'magnets' tend to 'glue' the structure together and give it stability. If I attempt to draw it for you (Fig 5), it will look just like a coiled piece of string. This is very misleading because the reality is more that of a string of sausages tangled up and pressed down into a soft round ball.

A language of three-letter words

The ribosome protein factory reads the language of messenger RNA in three-letter words. Each three-letter word is the cell's

Fig 5: How twenty amino acids in a string form structures

A.

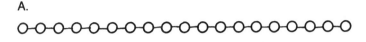

B.

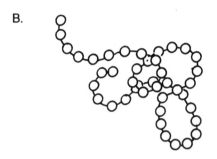

Note: the coiling is seen here only in two dimensions. In real life the coiling also happens towards and away from you in three dimensions. Many such shapes can be seen in the Science Museum in London where they display some of the original models built by scientists to try and work out the structure of proteins.

own name for one of twenty amino acids. The ribosome starts at the beginning of the RNA sequence and reads it triplet by triplet and, as it does, the factory increases the length of the amino acid chain block by block. As the chain begins to emerge it starts to fold up into the correct shape (Figs 6 and 7).

You will see from Fig 6 that like human language, the cell sometimes has several words that mean the same thing. These are used interchangeably. As soon as the forklift truck latches onto the RNA, an enzyme automatically joins the amino acid to the growing chain and disconnects it from the truck. The process moves along the RNA to the next word and repeats until it meets the UAA, UAG or UGA words which are cell language for 'stop'.

Fig 6: The Dictionary of Life

Each sequence of three bases is read by the ribosome factory as the word for one of twenty amino acid building blocks—the one to be added next.

UUU	Phenylalanine	AUU	Isoleucine
UUC	Phenylalanine	AUC	Isoleucine
UUA	Leucine	AUA	Isoleucine
UUG	Leucine	AUG	Methionine
UCU	Serine	ACU	Threonine
UCC	Serine	ACC	Threonine
UCA	Serine	ACA	Threonine
UCG	Serine	ACG	Threonine
UAU	Tyrosine	AAU	Asparagine
UAC	Tyrosine	AAA	Lysine
UAA	Full stop	AAG	Lysine
UAG	Full stop	AGU	Serine
UGU	Cysteine	AGC	Serine
UGC	Cysteine	AGA	Arginine
UGA	Full stop	AGG	Arginine
UGG	Tryptophan	AAC	Asparagine
CUU	Leucine	GUU	Valine
CUC	Leucine	GUC	Valine
CUA	Leucine	GUA	Valine
CUG	Leucine	GUG	Valine
CCU	Proline	GCU	Alanine
CCC	Proline	GCC	Alanine
CCA	Proline	GCG	Alanine
CCG	Proline	GAU	Aspartic acid
CAU	Histidine	GAC	Aspartic acid
CAC	Histidine	GAA	Glutamic acid
CAA	Glutamine	GAG	Glutamic acid
CAG	Glutamine	GGU	Glycine
CGU	Arginine	GGC	Glycine
CGC	Arginine	GGA	Glycine
CGA	Arginine	GGG	Glycine
CGG	Arginine	GCA	Alanine

Fig 7: A ribosome factory building a protein

Note: Here the triplet being read is UUU which you will see from the cell dictionary in Fig 6 is the code for an amino acid known by human chemists as phenylalanine. The assembly process is entirely automated. There are sixty-one different transporters or 'forklift trucks', each of which exactly fits only one of the sixty-one combinations of three bases used in the cell dictionary.

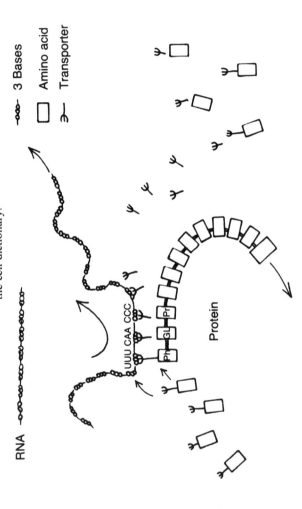

3 Bases

☐ Amino acid

⟩— Transporter

Proteins, fats and sugars to order

Some very complicated structures are formed from several different polypeptide chains—insulin for example is formed from two, and antibodies which are immensely important in medicine, as we will see, are formed from four.

Structures formed from sugars and fats cannot be programmed directly by the nucleus as ribosomes can only handle amino acids. To make these other things, the nucleus tells the ribosomes to produce special proteins called enzymes. These biological machines carry out simple tasks like building sugars or fats, or breaking them down in the process of digestion.

Having looked around inside a living cell and caught a glimpse of the huge range of activities going on, we can begin to understand why people want to use cells as mini-factories in a new biotech age. A single cell almost invisible to the naked eye can be used to carry out complex tasks which otherwise would require a huge laboratory with several people. All we have to do to take control of a cell is get the right message to a ribosome by placing the right gene inside the nucleus.

Dividing cells—duplicating genes

There is one other thing we must understand before we can go any further in moving from a single cell under our control to a massive chemical production factory using billions of these cells: how do cells divide, and how do they keep their genetic code the same each time?

The process is similar to what happens when messenger RNA is formed from DNA. The coiled structure of the DNA first has to straighten out. Next it is unzipped by an enzyme running from top to bottom. All the natural joins are broken (Fig 8).

The cell is very vulnerable to interference at this stage and mistakes can happen in the copying process. If they do occur the result is a mutation, although the effects may be so slight as to be unnoticeable because they are not in a critical part of the DNA sequence. Many mutations are lethal to the cell—the cell gets stuck mid-division or the mutation damages some vital function, while other mutations may cause disease.

Fig 8: How DNA is unzipped for cell division

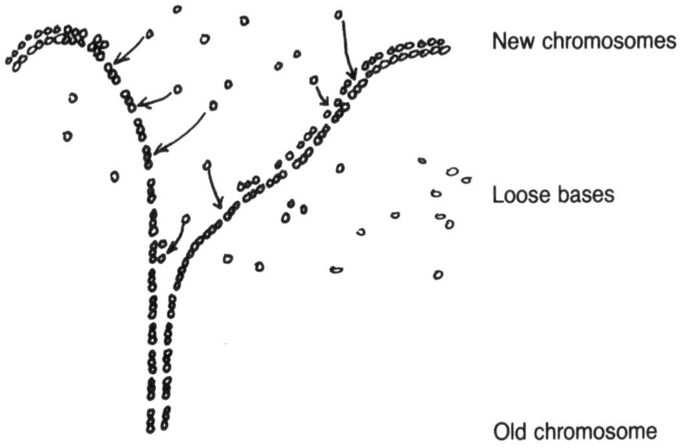

New chromosomes

Loose bases

Old chromosome

Note: As the DNA unzips, loose bases in the liquid of the nucleus get attracted to their opposite numbers and the result is two new double strands, each identical to the one before.

Mutations cause cancers and kill

Other mutations may cause more serious problems. A lethal mutation is harmless because only one cell dies out of millions, but a non-lethal mutation can kill the whole body by causing cancers. These can develop if genes are damaged, causing cells to lose touch with their neighbours and to divide inappropriately.

Cancer chemotherapy hits all growing cells by jamming the dividing mechanism. This can be done by giving someone with cancer a slightly altered base as a medicine. The base is used by growing cells to build new DNA, but the process halts when an incorrectly shaped building block is used.

Radiotherapy also attacks dividing cells—this time by firing atomic particles at high speed into a mass of dividing cells. The atomic particles knock out bases, preventing the cells from dividing properly and causing them to die. The treatment can of course slightly increase the risks of cancer developing in normal cells in the future.

Turning on your genes

Now we understand how cells work and divide, and how we can control them, we can start programming them for our biotech factory. However, one big problem remains. Just because genes have been inserted it does not mean that they will be active.

As we have seen most cells use only a tiny fraction of their total genes. The rest of the genes are turned off permanently although sometimes activated in certain diseases. The process of gradually turning off more and more genes, and turning on just a few, results in many different kinds of cells with specialist functions. This is called differentiation and usually happens before birth. For example, a nerve cell will always be a nerve cell. In other words, the destiny of each cell is determined in the womb. Cells influence each other by complex chemical signals in the developing embryo. These messages lock away huge sections of genetic code permanently.[16]

Passing on new genes to your children

It is essential to remember here the difference between *somatic* cells, which are fixed for a lifetime in one place or at one job, with a complete set of genes, and *germ* cells (sperm and eggs) which have half of each unzipped chromosome without duplication. Germ cells have only half the normal number of chromosomes and cannot divide until the other half is provided at fertilisation.

The genetic engineer has two choices: he can alter somatic cells with a limited effect in one organ until the organism dies, or he can alter germ cells so that every cell in the new embryo is reprogrammed. Germ cell changes are highly controversial because they will be passed on from generation to generation for ever. Scientists in many countries are already trying out a wide range of such experiments on animals.[17]

Many experts accept that with current rates of progress it will only be a matter of time before human germ cells are being altered routinely.[18] This raises huge ethical problems[19] which we will return to in Chapter 10.

Cloning simpler than changing genes

However, before we bother altering genetic code, how about simply copying it to produce an identikit clone or perfect twin? Surprising though it may seem, the technology of Aldous Huxley's *Brave New World* is already widely available, widely accepted and routinely used in animal breeding. So are humans any different or will the same techniques work to clone us too?

3

Giving Birth to Yourself—Human Cloning

Cloning animals is routine

One science fiction nightmare has long been to give people the power to create carbon copies or identical twins of themselves.[20] The technology is already here, and so are growing concerns about its use.[21] It is in fact far easier to copy all the genetic code of a cell than it is to rewrite it—at least you know the code works and what it will do. Even easier than copying is to get the body to do the copying for you.

Since all cells in the body, except red blood cells and germ cells, have an identical nucleus containing all the individual's genes, we have an unlimited source of complete chromosome sets we can use. Even simpler, we could transplant the entire nucleus from one cell into another using a microfine glass pipette (hollow glass needle).

The technology for injecting a single microscopic cell has been well established for many years.[22] The middle of a hollow piece of glass tubing is heated in a flame while pulling at both ends. As the glass softens, the two ends suddenly shoot apart. The middle becomes thinner and smaller until finally it is hundreds of times thinner than a human hair, and snaps. It is fascinating to watch it happen. You are left with two pieces of glass tubing which taper off at one end to microscopic size. The tubing is then attached to a microscope with special knobs and tiny levers, which can be used to position it precisely in an individual cell.

New pigs, sheep, rabbits, cows and chickens

For many years, we have been able to clone animals including pigs, sheep, rabbits, cows and chickens. In fact as we will see in later chapters we seem able to clone just about any mammal we have turned our energies to cloning.

To produce a clone, we need to be able to get hold of a complete set of chromosomes and put them into an egg and see what happens. It is easy to do this on a frog's egg because the nucleus is so large—you can see nuclei as the black dots in fresh frogspawn. As we have seen, this nucleus contains only half a set of chromosomes and would not give instructions to divide until the other half is provided by a sperm at fertilisation.

How to clone your favourite animal

However, with somewhat greater difficulty, we can borrow a complete set of chromosomes by taking a whole nucleus out of a skin cell. The skin nucleus is very small and the procedure is not easy. If we now inject the skin nucleus into an egg (nuclear transplantation) then a remarkable transformation happens:[23] the nucleus wakes up to the fact that it is no longer in a determined cell, and pulls all the volumes of the encyclopedia off the shelf at once. The nucleus instructs the cell to divide repeatedly to form an embryo (see Fig 9). The first successful clone was made this way in 1961 by Dr John Gurdon in Oxford.

Interestingly, if you want to save all the fuss and bother, you can make yourself a cheap cloning system by separating individual cells off before the big ball develops. If you do, each single cell taken away will carry on as if it is the only cell in the world and will go on dividing like a brand new fertilised egg. This technique is called blastomere separation (see Fig 10).

Prize bulls may become obsolete

Robbing early dividing groups of cells to produce clones has worked well recently for a variety of animals, especially cows and sheep.[24] Why bother to mate a magnificent prize cow with

Fig 9: How to clone a frog

1. Unfertilised egg
   (half set
   chromosomes)

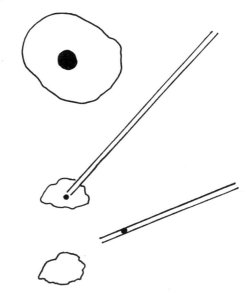

2. Skin cell nucleus
   removed into glass
   pipette

3. Skin cell nucleus
   injected into egg
   with or without
   removing egg
   nucleus first

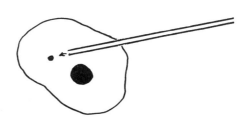

4. Egg begins to
   divide to develop
   exact twin (clone) of
   adult skin donor

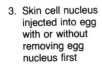

a second-rate bull? Why not just clone the freak high-output, high-meat-yield cow and insert these egg-like dividing cells into dozens of other cows to act as surrogate mothers for the clones? Cloning has already become a standard breeding technique.

The market for embryos is well developed. Farmers are well used to ordering frozen embryos for new breeds, to be grown in existing livestock, using them as surrogates. You will find embryos for sale at any large agricultural show in the UK. However, these are not yet clones, but embryos produced from individual sperm and eggs.

The days of prize bulls or stallions mating or even donating sperm may be numbered. Any animal can in theory be cloned this way. Obviously it takes a lot of skill to detach healthy dividing cells after fertilisation and insert them into wombs at the right time, and there is a limit to the number of clones you can make for each fertilised egg. We used to be able to work this method only up to the eight cell stage in mammals,[25] but the limit is growing all the time.

The reason is that until the developing ball of cells has properly implanted, the resulting cells tend to get smaller each time they divide because there is less food left in each. Taking one cell out of the ball to form a new ball is going to result in a smaller second ball of cells and a weakened embryo, which may not be viable.

Many of the techniques being used here—for example invitro fertilisation and embryo replacement—have been routine in infertility clinics and in farming for a number of years, although animal cloning has unexpectedly produced a few freak monsters (see page 92).[26]

Cloning humans may have started

So what are the practicalities of cloning humans? I have met a scientist in the UK who claims he has already cloned a human embryo.[27] He found his embryos were dying early—I suspect this was because he was using animals as surrogates and the surrogates were rejecting human embryos. Cloning of humans is specifically outlawed in the UK under the Human Fertilisation

Fig 10: How to make eight clones at once

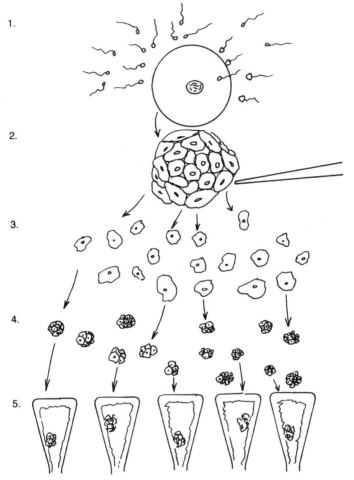

1. Egg and sperm mixed in test-tube.
2. Fertilised egg starts to form a ball of cells.
3. Ball broken up into separate cells.
4. Each cell starts again from the beginning.
5. Each ball of cells placed in a surrogate womb at the right stage of the menstrual cycle—resulting in numerous, cloned offspring.

and Embryology Act 1990. However, regulations are one thing; persuading every scientist to abide by them is another. Meanwhile many other countries have no controls at all.

So is there a market for human clones? I am deliberately asking this question laying aside any ethical considerations for the moment. The question is important here and in every other level of genetic engineering. If there is a market for human clones then they are likely to be made somewhere. Even if there is no commercial market for human clones they may still be created, probably on a more experimental scale, limited only by the conscience of the experimenter.

Unfortunately, global experience in war and peace shows us that such vast cultural and individual differences exist in worldview and personal ethics between individuals and nations, that somewhere at some time scientists will pursue what is physically possible, however undesirable. Such exploration may be for its own sake because such things are a challenge and intellectually fascinating, or it may be driven by personal philosophical, religious, moral or political persuasions.

The potential market for human clones is huge—especially if they can be frozen (and they can) and only produced some years after the death of the clone donor.

A child with built-in guarantees

If couples can opt for a donated egg and sperm from parents with known characteristics to be inserted into the mother's womb, why not cut out the uncertainties and go for a child with a complete set of guarantees?
* guaranteed intelligence
* guaranteed free from genetic diseases
* guaranteed abilities in other areas
You could even have a series of photographs showing what the child would look like aged one day, two years, six years, twelve years and as an adult.

Studies of identical twins separated at birth and brought up in very different families show extraordinary similarities in development, with similar tastes in dress, music and hobbies.

Similar career choices, partner choices, sexual orientation and mannerisms have also been noted.[28] Twin studies tell us just how much of what we are is influenced by our genes and how much by environmental factors. It is almost as if there is a gene memory system that tells us things about ourselves we need to know.

We see this most easily in animals such as birds which have complicated rituals and behaviours that we call instinct. These have been passed down in genes, not learned from observation. It is likely that humans are far more influenced by our own instincts than we like to think, and that as in animals, gene instincts favouring survival have been best preserved.[29]

The only thing that would not be guaranteed in a cloned embryo for sale would be the right environment for the child so that his or her guaranteed genetic potential could flourish best. However, we could describe in the advertising brochure an environment which usually produces excellent results with this particular set of genes. A horrific science fiction film recently portrayed a genetic engineer reconstructing Hitler's genetic code—not so difficult if a frozen tissue sample were found. However, the scientist realised that the death of Hitler's father had had a marked influence on his development. Therefore the child's 'father' was murdered to allow appropriate development.

Past dictators wishing to guarantee the survival of some aspect of their own personalities have sometimes sought to do so by conceiving large numbers of children. Cloning could be very appealing—possibly 'irresistibly' tempting—to a dictator wanting a son and heir worthy of his destiny. For someone obsessed with a sense of his own self, it could indeed be a fascinating adventure to watch himself grow up again forty years younger.

Let us argue, for the sake of exposing the controversy, that it is in fact no different from having a child who seems to have inherited mainly from one parent: 'He is so like his father.'

What is so unnatural about twins?

Here is another thought: would you be able to spot a clone if you met one? The answer is probably no, unless you are a member of the same family and have access to the photograph album. It should be pointed out here that naturally occurring identical twins also have a totally identical genetic code and are clones of each other.

Triplets may also be natural clones. In our example of adult cloning, the only thing that makes it unnatural is that these identical embryos have births separated by possibly fifteen, twenty or even fifty years. The other difference is that they are to be born with different parents—or apparently so.

Time-warp twins already born

We already store fertilised human eggs routinely, in liquid nitrogen at −196°C. By implanting such eggs eighteen months apart, twins have been born with different ages. In this case the twins were not identical because they developed from two different eggs fertilised at the same moment.[30]

Detecting clones will be hard

It could be argued that since environment has such a huge influence on development, the only identicalness would be in appearance at each stage compared to old photographs of the clone donor. In fact, due to age differences, donor and clone would probably never even look identical. Even if they were similar in age and looked and sounded the same, one might ask, 'What is so unnatural anyway about twins?' Natural clones exist in virtually every family tree.

We may react strongly to some of these suggestions, but unless we understand the ways these issues are likely to be presented we will be wholly unprepared to meet the issues of tomorrow's world—a world approaching faster than most people realise. Genetic engineers are swift to point out technical difficulties, but in fact they are no different from the difficulties of cloning any other mammal. It is the ethical difficulties that are so vast.

New parts for old bodies

There is another more hideous (yet also potentially lifesaving) aspect of cloning: using a clone to manufacture a new organ.

Earlier we saw that cells in an embryo quickly sense their position in the body and become more and more specialised. In theory it should be possible to take a semi-specialised cell developed from a fertilised egg and treat it in the laboratory so that it reacts to form, say, a perfect replacement kidney.

A simpler approach already being used in medicine is to collect aborted foetuses in an operating theatre and then surgically remove various organs and tissues for transplanting into people who need them. Needless to say, the practice, although increasingly common, has not been widely publicised.[31]

Humans looking to buy spares

Why is there a demand for foetal or clone transplants? Spare-part surgery only works if spares are available, and if spare parts work after replacement. Unfortunately for many who die each year of kidney, heart or other organ failure, not only are spares often not available, but they also often fail to work for a number of reasons. Spares are often unavailable because tissues or organs need ideally to be moved instantaneously from one living body into another. The nearest we get to this is the living donor: a parent who donates a kidney to a child for example.

In these cases, two surgical teams operate at the same time on donor and recipient in adjacent operating theatres. Sometimes unrelated donors have been paid, located through newspaper advertisements—a practice frowned on but impossible to stop. Such adverts are legal in many countries. The going rate for a kidney is around £3,000 paid for an operation in the UK, and £1,000 in a developing country such as India.[32]

A recent scandal involved a British surgeon and a Turkish donor who spoke no English and was said to be unaware of what was going on. Several previous cases occurred in 1985 involving patients from the Indian sub-continent who brought donors with them, claiming they were relatives. After the kidney trade was exposed by a UK newspaper, the surgeon went to India to discover to his horror that the donors had been paid, were unrelated and lived in squalor, most of the money having gone to the 'kidney merchants'. As a result of this case the

Human Organ Transplantation Act was passed in 1989, banning such practices here, while they continue to be legal elsewhere.

'Kidney for sale' adverts in press

However, laws do not prevent people from doing what they want. They just provide a means of punishment when they are found out, hopefully acting as a deterrent to others. In the subsequent Turkish scandal, a UK doctor had been faced with a series of dying patients with seemingly bottomless bank accounts. He asked a Turkish friend to contact a relative in Istanbul, telling him to answer classified adverts in Turkish newspapers from people offering to sell their own kidneys— even though trading in human organs is illegal there too. A donor was located and flown over to the UK for a wealthy Israeli client. Operations took place in adjoining operating theatres. Other operations followed. The doctor who organised these donations was later struck off the Medical Register.[33] He said afterwards: 'If the patients had not been transplanted they would have been dead.'[34]

One kidney specialist said recently: 'Ethics is what you believe this year. At an international conference I heard an argument from a US specialist, that if you're Bangladeshi and can sell your kidney and thereby secure the survival of your sixteen children, why not?'[35] Another defence argument goes that a father can donate to his son, but if his kidney is not compatible he should be able to sell it to someone else instead, using the money to buy a compatible one from some-one else. While the operation itself carries a slight risk, life insurance premiums are no higher for someone with a single kidney because the absence of one is not considered to be dangerous.[36]

Shortage of spare kidneys

In many cases, where organs could be donated, death has occurred with loss of circulation to the tissues and accumulation of poisonous substances before they can be removed. In the case of donated corneas or skin grafts, the timing is not so critical. Corneas can survive body death for a number of hours.

Their need of food and oxygen is low and such transplants are relatively straightforward.

Kidneys, however, work extremely hard at all times in the body, purifying the blood. Kidney cells are damaged permanently in half an hour unless the kidney is rapidly chilled after removal by storage in an ice box. Kidney donors tend therefore to be accident victims where massive brain destruction has occurred. The person is effectively deceased, but the heart, lungs and kidneys are all still functioning, with machines artificially maintaining the body in the twilight zone between life and full death.

Therefore kidney donation is usually accompanied by a decision to turn off a life-support machine. The numbers of kidneys available fell dramatically recently after a series of television programmes which caused great public uncertainties about whether or not such accident victims were truly dead. Fears that pressures to transplant could over-ride a small chance of recovery led to many relatives refusing to give permission and to large numbers of people tearing up their kidney donor cards. There is still an acute shortage.

Over 7,000 people suffer kidney failure annually in the UK alone, and 2,000 are turned away to die due to shortages of dialysis facilities. Although 1,800 kidney transplants take place in the UK each year, the waiting list is around 3,700. At least eight out of ten kidneys implanted go on working successfully for three years or more, so the whole process is very worthwhile.[37]

Human spares may not fit

However, even if sufficient organs are available there is often a further major limitation to spare-part surgery: compatibility of tissues between donor and recipient. As we have seen, each person's set of genes is a quite unique combination of tens of thousands of individual messages. Just as each person's facial features are different, so also are the surface features of each cell in the body.

The area where we are most familiar with cell surface variation is in giving or receiving blood. There are several main blood groupings, each of which is incompatible with the others. For this reason the blood type of both donor and recipient is always checked before transfusion. However, if you were to receive a kidney from someone with the same blood group, your body would almost certainly reject it as foreign and destroy it.

Incidentally there are clearly huge advantages in having some parts of genetic code which are constant—for example the design of the eye—and others which vary infinitely between people—for example facial appearance. Indeed the whole basis of social interaction relies on us being able to tell individuals apart and to recognise each other. Since facial features are a result of our varying genes, perhaps one day we will be able to produce an exact photofit of a wanted criminal from a tissue sample found at the scene of the crime.[38]

World market for fresh organs

Very occasionally, you find two people whose cell features are so similar that a transplant would be accepted well. With identical twins, of course, by definition every organ donation will be a perfect match. Finding these matches between all organ donors and people needing them is extremely complicated and explains why, as we have seen, organs are often flown great distances to find the person with the best match. It also explains why commercial pressures have resulted in people buying and selling kidneys, and in paying non-relatives to donate them.[39]

Genetic research is contributing to our understanding of these cell differences and how to overcome them.[40] Badly matching organs usually fail rapidly, although high doses of steroids and other treatments can be used to try and persuade the body's defences to tolerate the transplant.

So spare parts are often not available and often do not work as well as we would like after a transplantation. Having said this, we are seeing great improvements with more sophisticated treatment after transplantation, and a great many alive today owe their survival to organ donation. The two which perhaps do best are kidneys, where kidney failure itself poisons the body's defences, so transplant rejection is often less, and cornea transplants, where the body's defences seem to tolerate new eye coatings very well.

Growing your own organ replacements

Having decided there could be a big market in self-grown replacement organs, how would it be done? First we have to look at work that has already been carried out in animals or using animals. In 1984 there was a huge outcry when a surgeon in Southern California removed the beating heart from a baboon and transplanted it into a baby known as 'Baby Fae'. For reasons which are obvious from what we have just seen, the heart was rejected and the baby died.

However, we are now seeing similar experiments in reverse: organs removed from late human foetuses that have just been aborted, and inserted into animals. These experiments are being carried out in Palo Alto, Mexico by a company backed by a $10 million investment.[41] They are using mice bred without any natural immune system to fight either infection or transplants from humans.

Foetal transplants into mice

The mice are kept in a strictly germ-free environment. Then they receive foetal human tissue—for example, thymus, lymph node or liver cells. With these transplants the mouse develops a human-style immune system. The mice can then be infected with the AIDS virus (HIV) or with other viruses which also fail to grow well other than in humans. The mice can then be used to test potentially hazardous new treatments. These humanised mice are big business, but may be flawed because the mice still do not develop human disease like we do.

Incidentally, there is another more serious problem: trying to infect mice with HIV could lead to a mutation, producing an even more dangerous version of HIV. This could happen if naturally occurring mouse viruses combined in some way with HIV. It has even been suggested by some scientists that such interspecies virus experiments could conceivably have led to the emergence of HIV in the first place.[42] Although the evidence appears to be stacked against this alarming suggestion (see Chapter 7), the fact that it can even be made shows some of the problems that can emerge. As we will see later on (page 113), experimental viruses have combined unexpectedly with each other in animals in the past, becoming more dangerous as the new strain emerged.

Foetal transplants for humans

We can reverse this method to treat humans. How about taking organs or tissue from animal foetuses and transferring them into humans? Such transplants will be rejected as surely as the monkey heart in the earlier example. But what about removing tissue from an aborted human foetus and using that instead? Such an idea may be abhorrent, but is it being done?

For several years now tissue from aborted foetuses has been used to treat patients with severe combined immunodeficiency disease.[43] Unlike AIDS, this is an inherited condition affecting all the immune system rather than just one part. The tissues transplanted are pieces of liver and parts of the bone marrow. In another related disease called the Di George Syndrome, the tissue transplanted is from the thymus gland. Other types of immunodeficiency, disorders of red blood cell production and disorders of metabolism can also be treated in this way.

Human foetuses to repair brains

Interestingly, although the foetal tissue is completely incompatible and would normally be rejected—no matching takes place between foetal donor and recipient—these transplants seem to work. Other uses are likely to be made of foetal transplants in the future. Over the last ten years a number of experiments have been carried out in animals using foetal tissue transplants to cure brain damage. Such experiments are an extension of nerve tissue transplants that have been studied for around 100 years.[44]

If these latest experiments prove successful then we can expect to see foetal brain or spinal cord transplants in humans. The hope would be to try and overcome a big problem in damaged human brains. Unlike the situation in the developing embryo, once a baby is born the nerve cells seem to stop dividing and seem to be incapable of repair—unlike skin, for example. By transplanting primitive brain cells we might be able to help the damaged brain to repair itself.[45]

Cloning a baby for spare kidneys

Let's take the hypothetical case of a dying prize-winning musician. He needs a kidney and none is available. He gives a blood sample and is told to come back in about eight to ten months' time for a transplant. He pays a very large sum for the privilege. The transplant is entirely successful. The only complication is that it takes quite a while to get going fully.

Without realising it, he has just paid a private clinic for a cloned kidney. A nucleus was taken from a white blood cell in the sample he gave, and inserted into a human egg, which in turn was implanted into a surrogate mother's womb. The mother was hired for a small fee from the streets of a developing country.[46] After nine months a cloned baby was removed by Caesarian section. Shortly after birth one kidney was removed and inserted into the musician. The baby was adopted twenty-four hours later by doting parents in another country, who were told that the child had been born with a defective kidney that had now been removed.

Wanted: surrogate mums and growth factor

Fact or fiction? As we have seen, the cloning technology is all there. The demand is certainly there. For the present there are two blocks: the first is obtaining a surrogate mother. However, that is becoming easier in the West if the right story is told and is probably impossible to prevent commercially in the two-thirds world. A mother could be offered the equivalent of ten years' wages (£10,000) by an agent.

Attitudes to surrogates are changing rapidly. In the UK the British Medical Association has shifted from condemning surrogacy in 1984 to accepting it as a normal part of treating infertility.[47] In this case it allows a couple to create an embryo with their own eggs and sperm, and then have it grown inside someone else to a normal baby. The baby is born and hopefully is returned. Technically under British law such a baby then needs to be adopted.

The process provides a child to parents when, say, the absence of a womb in the mother would otherwise have prevented pregnancy. Such a child is 100% genetically derived from the 'adoptive' parents, although variations in the arrangements can allow semen from the father to fertilise the surrogate mother's egg, producing a child only half derived genetically from the new parents.

The latest British Medical Association guidelines suggest that surrogacy should only be assisted if all other infertility approaches have failed, and if the 'commissioning couple' are suitable as adoptive parents. It is also suggested that the surrogate mother and the adoptive parents should not know each other—to avoid problems when the child is born.

Recently, the mother of a seventeen-year-old leukaemia victim decided to have another baby in order to use the baby as a donor of bone marrow for her sick daughter. If the baby turned out to be a girl, the chances were 99% in favour that the donation would be successful. The US mother took this step after all efforts to locate a donor failed, recognising that although the operation would involve the baby in some pain, it would not affect its future health or wellbeing. The case caused great unease: what if cancer centres joined with fertility clinics to mass-produce embryos for tissue-matching purposes? What if babies conceived in this way and operated on were then regarded as surplus and offered for adoption?[48]

The second larger block is that a newborn baby kidney is much too small and immature to help a full-grown adult much. However, other tissues might do rather better, in particular bone marrow and other rapidly dividing organs such as skin to cover grossly disfiguring burns, for example (see page 110).

Perhaps having at least formed a complete baby kidney in the uterus we will in the future be able to accelerate its growth in the laboratory using new growth hormones while connecting it to an artificial blood supply. The skin example is an interesting one because we are able in this case to clone skin directly from skin cells—without having to create a whole new human being.

Skin cells can be stimulated to grow and divide. They can be tricked into thinking that they are on the edge of the wound. In the laboratory, large sheets of skin can be grown quite rapidly from just a few sample pieces. These can then be returned to the donor. We are also able to clone cells successfully from bone marrow as a routine part of medical treatment in those with leukaemia.

Cannibalising a baby twin

Another approach is to plan spare parts for a human before it has even been born. A Cambridge embryologist has commented:

> The ultimate step along this path would be reached when a newly fertilized egg was divided into two cells, one would be grown to the appropriate stage and then implanted into a woman, thus becoming in time the definitive human being; the other would be kept in a state of suspended animation in the frozen state. If the adult human being at some period during his life was in need of an organ transplant, the frozen embryo could be implanted into a mother's uterus, and, after birth, it could be allowed to grow until its organs were in a suitable state to be cannibalised for the sake of its more fortunate brother.[49]

So cloning is here to stay as a breeding technique for farmers, and is becoming a reality for parents. It is relatively simple, cheap and reliable—so long as the original is what you want. But how do we make a new model from which to clone, with unique features never seen before in the history of the earth?

4

Gene Machines

If we have cracked the code of life, and are able to make new genes, can we start designing animals, plants or even humans in the same way as we design new chips for computers? How do you produce a new species to order? Are there any limits to the options open to biodesigners? Can we design machines to do it all automatically?

Patents for new humans

You can see how important creating new species is becoming by the intense legal debate over whether or not a new species can be patented. Patenting is a legal device to record ownership of an invention. It prevents anyone else from using it except under licence. Patents are usually valid for seventeen to twenty years. Patent applications are driven by huge commercial interests.

Patents on life forms are not new. As early as 1873, the US Patent Office granted a patent to Louis Pasteur for a new yeast. Patents for new microbes do not seem to cause as much public concern as patents on plants, animals, or even humans. In 1980, in an historic decision, the US Patent Office declared that 'anything under the sun that is made by man' is patentable.[50]

In 1987 the US Patent Office announced that higher life forms could be patented, and in 1988 the first animal became patented: the cancer-prone 'oncomouse' now 'owned' by Harvard University. However, a 'master' patent on a genetically engineered protein has twice been overturned by British courts recently.[51] The European Community seems likely to pass a law treating certain animals and plants as genetic inventions, protected under patent since approving the 'oncomouse' in 1991.[52]

In 1990 the European Patent Office refused to grant patents on human beings, although an exception was made for human genes.[53] Meanwhile US Congress has been debating whether or not human beings can be patented as inventions in a similar way.[54] Genetic research 'will produce beings who fall halfway between what we currently think of as "animal" and "human". It is unclear on which side of the legal line these creatures will fall.'[55]

How do you define a human being?

In April 1988 US Congress eventually decided that human beings could not for the moment be patented. However, there was no clear definition of what exactly constitutes a human being. After all, how much genetic code do you have to change? It is all very well to say that human beings cannot be patented, but as we have seen, the only thing worth patenting is the contents of a single human nucleus containing altered DNA.

What about growing altered human cells in a laboratory flask? If these genes were transplanted into an egg, a new human strain could emerge. Therefore by patenting genetic code in single human cells it may be possible effectively to patent a human being legally already in some countries.

Meanwhile, the European Patent Office received an application in 1992 to patent human breasts by a backdoor route involving sheep. An American medical college and a biotechnology company wanted to protect a method of producing pharmaceutical products in the mammary glands of all mammals including humans. In the same week a British company signed a £10 million deal to allow a German firm to commercialise drugs secreted in the milk of a genetically engineered Scottish sheep called Tracy.[56]

Patents to protect investment

This is a vitally important area requiring a global legal framework in our global village. It also requires those writing legislation and voting on it to be fully informed. The problem of definitions is going to make effective laws increasingly difficult to write. Meanwhile, constraints on gene research are becoming fewer in the US following the disbanding of the human gene therapy subcommittee of the US National Institutes of Health.[57] Part of the reason for this is to make it easier for companies to develop biotech products, encouraging them to continue to stay in the US.

Without the legal protection of patents many companies are unwilling to invest heavily. Twenty years' research could be lost overnight. All a farmer would have to do is get hold of one altered plant or animal from which breeding could take place, and with the right technical support new perfect copies could be cloned indefinitely.[58] Without a patent there would be no way to stop 'genetic theft'. The effect could be similar to robbing a computer software company by copying a floppy disk containing an expensive computer program.

Is it right to own life?

Such laws are raising immense ethical concerns on both sides of the Atlantic with a group called Patent Concern, formed in Europe in early 1991 and representing more than thirty environmental, animal, welfare and religious groups including Greenpeace, the RSPCA, the Genetics Forum and Christian Aid.[59] Animal welfare is an issue because some of these animal 'inventions' are literally designed to suffer—for example the cancer-suffering oncomouse mentioned above and used extensively in cancer research.[60]

In June 1991 the Nuffield Foundation in the UK set up a new Council on Bioethics under Sir Patrick Nairne to address moral and ethical issues. However, as we shall see, all this activity comes rather late in the day, following a long way behind what scientists are actually doing.[61] We will look more closely at the whole issue of law and regulations in Chapter 9.

Once laws have begun operating in various countries[62] giving companies the right to own different species of plants or animals, massive legal disputes between companies have followed, trying to prove who first created the new genetic code for a new plant or animal.[63]

However, patent protection is one thing; having the licence to manufacture or to sell is quite another, with some countries proposing or implementing bans or delaying permission pending investigations,[64] even where patents have been formally registered. This whole area is becoming increasingly political.[65]

The problem with patents on plants or animals is that in theory a farmer would have to pay a licence fee for every reproduction. For example, every time a calf was born on the farm, it would become the property of the licence holder unless the birth was officially allowed under a permit.[66] As we shall see later, patents on animals or crops could have terrible consequences for developing countries, who could have to pay wealthy nations a royalty on every sack of grain or every animal born.

Designer genes

Assuming for the moment we lay aside all ethical and legal debates, there are several approaches we can take to designing life. They all work by treating genetic code as a language text on a computer in exactly the same way that this book was programmed onto a word processor.

With a word processor I can alter this book in various ways: I can delete text and retype just the bits I want to change. I can of course wipe out the whole thing and retype it from scratch. There is another interesting feature of the word processor which allows the writer to borrow sections of text from elsewhere. For example, text from a previously published magazine article can be lifted out and inserted into another document.

Needle in a haystack

All these same techniques can be used by the genetic writer. Writing from scratch works all right if the piece is short and you know what you are doing. Deleting or inserting a minor change is also possible. Inserting a large chunk of genetic writing from elsewhere (another organism) also works well, and is the simplest thing to do. After all, at least you know the code inserted has some biological effects in at least one species.

However, the genetic writer still suffers from a massive disadvantage. So little of the encyclopedia of life has been translated, that looking for a particular gene with a particular effect is like looking for a needle in a haystack. One of the easiest ways to reprogram cells without having to decipher code is to use enzymes to cut up DNA into hundreds of random fragments, and insert each into bacteria to see what happens.[67]

Insulin from genes

A good example has been the search for the gene controlling insulin production, in order to find a better treatment for diabetes. Insulin is needed by the body to use sugars properly. In those with diabetes, the Langerhans cells in the pancreas no longer produce sufficient insulin. Without insulin, sugar is absorbed into the blood from food, but does not cross cell walls, so people lack energy, cannot think clearly and can even die. Insulin can be extracted from the pancreas of cows or pigs, but it contains impurities which the body reacts to. Nevertheless, such extracts have successfully treated diabetics for many years.

Can we find the genetic code for insulin? Can we then program new cells to make pure human insulin? The first job is to find the gene for insulin. Thousands of pieces of human genetic code of varying lengths have been inserted into bacteria to see what happens. Each fragment has been copied thousands of times using an automated simple-to-use laboratory machine.[68]

Once fragments of genetic code have been copied sufficiently and then separated, a vehicle is needed to carry one piece at a time into bacteria. Bacteria are simple single-celled organisms that live, breathe, sometimes move, and produce not only gases such as carbon dioxide but often poisonous substances as well. The type of bacteria usually used in experiments is called

E. coli, a relatively harmless germ that lives in the gut and helps us digest our food.

Viruses carry new genes

Bacteria, like humans, get all kinds of viral infections. Bacterial viruses are called plasmids and work by transferring new genetic code from one bacteria into another.[69] Human viruses do the same. The AIDS virus, HIV, for example inserts new genetic code into the soldier cells (T4 white cells) that your body uses to fight infection. When the genetic code is added to the chromosomes in the nucleus, the soldier cell effectively loses the instruction sheets on fighting infection and gains instruction sheets on making new virus particles.

Plasmids have been studied a lot in the laboratory.[70] We know a great deal about them because bacteria pass pieces of genetic messages to each other all the time in the human gut using plasmids. If a few bacteria become resistant to a new antibiotic, the genetic secret of how they manage it quickly travels to other gut bacteria, so the other types of bacteria also quite literally learn new ways of avoiding damage from the antibiotic. This is a very important reason why many doctors now try to avoid using antibiotics unless they really need to—we do not want to end up educating a load of plasmids.

Plasmids are everywhere

Plasmids do in fact exist very widely in the environment and their effects are seen particularly in places where bacteria are adapting to new habitats or where their environment is changing. Plasmids are particularly found in excreta from man and animals where antibiotics have been used, where antibiotics find their way into sewage (often excreted unchanged in urine or as a result of, say, disposing of unwanted medicines down the drain), or from industrial contamination. Industrial discharges containing toxic heavy metals will also induce plasmid-led adaptations.[71]

Incidentally, industrial wastes produced as a side-product of the chemical industry are becoming more and more of a problem to dispose of safely. Increasingly the industry is looking to genetic engineers to produce bacteria to eat these toxic substances,[72] breaking them down into non-toxic residues.[73]

Bacteria to eat toxic waste

One example recently has been the problem of what to do with tens of thousands of East German cars called Trabants. These were produced prior to the collapse of the Eastern bloc with the opening of travel restrictions to the West. Much loved by some and hated by others, these primitive two-cylinder cars are highly wasteful of petrol and fill the air with higher than normal concentrations of polluting gases.

However, the biggest problem of all is presented by what they are made of. Unlike most cars in the West, the bodies of Trabants are made of a synthetic resin which does not rot or rust and cannot be burned because burning releases highly toxic gases. A recent newspaper report claimed that genetic engineers were working on a new type of microbe to eat these vehicles, turning the bodies into a harmless sludge.[74] These changes will also be made using plasmids.

A new plague of bacterial viruses

Returning to the problems of plasmids being released or multiplying in the environment, we find that prior to the antibiotic revolution in farming and medicine, plasmids were relatively uncommon. Now their distribution as bacterial viruses is vast in both land and water environments, including the sea.

Recent research off the east coast of the US has suggested that these viruses are now multiplying in their tens of billions to form such concentrations that, even in seawater, their density is enough to transfer data from one bacterium to another.[75] Concentrations were ten million times what they had expected to find. This has big implications for safety since it appears genetically modified bacteria could exchange genes with 'wild' bacteria in seawater to produce a wide range of hybrids, with unpredictable consequences.

How to make bacteria more human

It is a relatively simple matter to place human genes into plasmids. Enormous advances have been made in the last two to three years.[76] Plasmids can then be mixed with bacteria. Very occasionally the results can be spectacular, although this is very much a hit-and-miss approach.

Bacteria can be separated easily by taking a metal probe and dipping it into a solution containing bacteria. The probe is then scraped in a zigzag pattern across a small dish containing a special jelly called agar. The dish is then placed in an incubator at blood temperature for several days. Towards the end of the zigzag pattern the number of bacteria still left on the probe is so low that only a very few bacteria end up on that part of the jelly. Each multiplies rapidly to form a small sticky mound, a few millimetres in diameter. Each of these mounds is an individual colony (a clone) from an individual bacterium.

If we add a special marker to the gene we are looking to test—such as a piece of code for antibiotic resistance—then we will immediately be able to spot the one in a hundred bacteria which have been successfully modified. They will be the only ones able to grow, forming colonies in agar mixed with antibiotic. These colonies can then be tested for any unusual properties which will tell us what activities are related to the piece of genetic code.

Success at last

After a great number of attempts, an extraordinary event took place: one of the reprogrammed bacteria began to make human insulin. Such an event only has to happen once in a long time to keep a whole laboratory of scientists happy for years. After all, a reprogrammed bacterium can now be cultured separately. Each time it divides it produces another insulin-producing organism. By filling a big brewery-style vat full of warm liquid and food, we can start off a process as large as brewing beer, except that in this case we are brewing insulin. It still needs careful extraction and purifying from other parts of the brew, however, to remove any dangerous substances from the mixture.

By the late 1980s bacteria were already being used routinely to produce the first genetically engineered 'pure' human insulin. This insulin has now almost entirely replaced cow and pig insulin, but with one or two problems emerging recently.[77] Many other remarkable successes have followed: for example, producing vast quantities of fragments of hepatitis B virus in a big fermentation vat, using a yeast called saccharomyces.[78] These particles are harmless but can be injected as a vaccine for hepatitis B. Industrial scale production of genetically engineered products is now commonplace.[79]

New ways to swop genes

Scientists have now perfected a somewhat different method for changing genetic code in mammal cells, called electroporation.[80] This uses a high voltage electrical discharge to make cell walls 'leaky' so that genetic code (DNA) in the surrounding liquid can find its way into the cell.[81] Around one in a hundred cells can be 'transfected' in this way.[82] This has an advantage over a number of other methods of reconstructing animal and plant cells—including microsurgery, the use of polyethylene glycol with a virus type called sendai,[83] or a technique known as erythrocyte ghost fusion.[84]

A much newer and more experimental technique fires genes at high speed into tissues using a special machine to accelerate micro-projectiles of tungsten metal coated with DNA. Mouse skin and liver cells have been reprogrammed using this 'biolistic' method. An advantage is that internal organs such as the liver can be treated through several cell layers without tissue damage. However, the genes are not integrated into the cell nucleus, so the effect lasts less than two weeks.[85] Another method tried recently has been to reprogram immature muscle cells (myoblasts) and inject them into muscle, where they live for several months, secreting whatever they have been reprogrammed to produce.[86]

Animals as chemical factories

Reprogrammed mammal cells can either be used like bacteria, growing them in a flask in a factory, or they can be transplanted back, turning the whole animal into a factory production unit. This has been tried in mice, reprogramming skin cells to produce Factor 9, needed to treat a blood disorder related to haemophilia.[87] Bacteria are only suitable for producing relatively simple substances. More complicated proteins require the extra machinery in mammal cells.[88]

These experiments have basically worked through the 'cut and paste' principle: cutting up a piece of text with a pair of scissors, inserting it into a different book altogether and seeing how it reads.[89] Similar progress has also been made on reprogramming yeasts (or fungi).

With bacteria, the results are usually obvious fairly quickly, but when genetically altering plants and/or animals, it can take months or years to tell if you have been successful or not. The plant or tree has to grow to produce a crop or fruit you can test, for example. However, there are ways of shortening the whole process. If you can find a marker, as we have seen in the earlier example, you are more than half way there.

How to detect success

As we have seen, markers are genes on the same strip of code, or very close to it, that produce an immediate, easily observed result, such as antibiotic resistance. An example currently being used for human cells is a gene which gives human cancer cells multidrug resistance to therapy. This is easy to spot if it is taken up by cells in the laboratory. If joined to a less immediately obvious gene we can tell rapidly if reprogramming with the second gene has been successful.[90] We do this by exposing cells we hope have been reprogrammed to the toxic chemicals. Those that survive are worth looking at further.

Learning to speak gene language

There is another possibility: how about actually learning to speak the language of the nucleus? We have learned a few words and phrases: for example we have deciphered the exact sequence of the gene that codes for insulin[91] and that for Factor 8 needed by those with haemophilia. The Factor 8 code, analysed in 1984, was an extraordinary feat since this massive gene was a full 0.1% of one entire chromosome.[92]

We have also identified and analysed the giant Duchenne muscular dystrophy gene which causes muscle wasting.[93] We have recently identified the gene that causes the most common type of inherited mental handicap: the fragile X syndrome (see page 98). This affects one in a thousand children, almost all boys, and causes mental retardation.[94]

Translating every human gene

Now a much more ambitious programme is under way: one of the most daunting scientific challenges ever attempted. The task is to write out the entire human genetic code, letter by letter from start to finish. The code as a whole is known as the human genome and as we have seen, it is millions of characters long. Many hundreds of research scientists in a number of countries are racing against time to crack this code of human life. When it is completed we will be able to begin to work out a vast dictionary showing the meaning in terms of function of each small word or sentence.

Human Genome Project

In the USA the National Institute of Health (NIH) has set aside £150 million for the Human Genome Project over the next two years, headed up until recently by James Watson, co-discoverer of DNA structure in 1953. He thinks it will take fifteen years, at a cost of £2,000,000,000.[95] James Watson resigned suddenly in 1992 after public concerns about his shareholdings in biotechnology companies and possible conflicts of interest.[96] The Director of Research at the Imperial Cancer Research Fund recently estimated that if the cost were spread over fifteen years, split between Europe, the Americas, Japan and Asia, this would give Europe a bill of £30 million a year, of which the UK might need to contribute £10 million a year.[97]

The Human Genome Organisation has 250 members from all over the world. The project could have huge commercial value for Western nations. The Medical Research Council and the Centre for Exploitation of Science and Technology (CEST) have recently set up a programme to help UK companies commercialise genetic discoveries—Europe is considered to be up to four years behind the USA.[98]

An expensive business

The Cystic Fibrosis Foundation alone is reported to have spent over £10 million on the Human Genome Project in the UK between 1985 and 1989.[99] As a direct result we now know the exact sequence of code for the fibrosis gene, after processing and analysing almost 300,000 letters of genetic writing. The discovery has huge implications for diagnosis and treatment.[100]

This vast cystic fibrosis project sequenced less than 0.01% of the total human genome of three billion characters. Who will own the information?[101] Already USA scientists have begun applying for patents for the bits of the genome they have deciphered. Reluctantly, scientists in the UK have begun to do the same, to protect British commercial interests. The initial US application has been refused but the verdict is being challenged.[102] Expert advice from patent agents has indicated that there is no outstanding reason why such applications should not succeed. The result could be to slow down research, because massive royalties will become due if successful new medical products are developed.

Such progress raises urgent ethical questions which we will look at later.[103]

Machines to read and write genes

Reading genetic code is immensely complicated—or rather it used to be. Sequencing work done by hand used to take months—just to decipher several thousand letters of code. Now a similar process takes less than a week and is almost entirely automatic—thanks to the computer technology of the previous decade. This whole field is known as microchemical instrumentation.[104] Of the 3,000,000,000 base pairs that make up the human genome, only a few million have so far been decoded. However, the new machines mean that a biologist can now sequence up to 15,000 base pairs a day or 5,000,000 a year. Relating sequences to different cell activities is a huge problem, made simpler by the latest pattern recognition computers which are now processing data collected from laboratories all over the world.[105]

Similar machines can now write code as well as read it. You can type in a sequence up to fifty characters long, press a button and come back in a few hours. The genetic code will be assembled and waiting for you. The machine is only the size of a desktop computer, and is available by mail order, advertised in many scientific magazines. The process used to be very laborious and experimental.[106] The machine works by adding different chemical solutions and enzymes one at a time, in a complex sequence. Each series of steps adds just one character of code.

Desktop gene machines

Kits to join genetic code strips together can also be bought cheaply, together with genetic code duplicators. These kits are not much larger in size than five copies of this book laid on top of each other. You can see these items on show at the Science Museum in London and even decode part of a gene yourself using a computer simulation.[107] A new computer program is also available now to help design new plasmids and to facilitate in cell cloning operations. The program is called Clone 3.[108] New methods are being developed continually to speed up and simplify the process from gene sequencing to reprogramming to the end result of protein production.[109]

One of the quickest ways to duplicate genetic code is known as the polymerase chain reaction.[110] The enzyme is found in a special bacterium that lives in the boiling water of hot springs and requires a high temperature to work.[111] It has revolutionised DNA technology, as it allows virtually any nucleic acid sequence (DNA) to be generated in the test-tube in large amounts. The DNA produced is pure, and the procedure is much faster than using cells to reproduce it. It is also about to become an important diagnostic tool in microbiology for detection of specific sequences. Practically even a single bacterium, virus particle or parasite can be detected by it,[112] and it can also be similarly used in forensic medicine to analyse samples or in archaeology to analyse plant or animal remains.[113]

Directory of human genes

A complete directory of all genes located in humans is now in its tenth edition and has 5,710 entries, of which 2,000 genes have been mapped to specific sites on chromosomes.[114] The implications will be beyond measure: if you consider the genetic code as a massive long line of on/off switches with labels, within the next two decades we should be able to engineer small changes precisely where we want and know what the result will be.

Monkeys with human speech?

Rapid progress in understanding our genetic makeup allows us to ask some very interesting questions about patterns of life; questions that may at first sight appear bizarre, but which are of fundamental importance to us in designing new species. Can farmers produce better animals for eating?[115] Do elephants have to be so large—can't we program miniature ones?

There is no logical or practical reason why we cannot give human genes to chimpanzees with the aim of giving them a spoken language capability and better reasoning powers. Perhaps we could use them as intelligent subhuman clones for difficult and dangerous tasks, instead of incredibly expensive and limited robots. Although we do not yet know which genes give us language ability, it can only be a matter of time before we have unravelled the answer.

Before we know where we are, we have returned to debating what constitutes a human being: how much human code do you need—5%, 10%, 55%? Is it just appearance? How human do you have to look? The issues do not just relate to patents, but more importantly to ethical licensing. Even to ask the questions is to risk arousing the most intense controversy.[116]

Defining what is human on the basis of genes has produced bizarre results. In 1978, Francis Crick, the Nobel Prize winning genetic scientist wrote: 'No infant should be declared human until it has passed certain tests regarding its genetic endowment. If it fails these tests, it forfeits the right to live.'[117]

By comparing the genomes of different people[118] and different animals, it should be possible to build up a vast vocabulary accurately. The interesting thing is the unity of the genetic code: a yeast cell uses exactly the same coding language as a human. Therefore the same technology works for reprogramming human cells or those from other mammals.[119]

Humans with a spare pair of hands?

One of the difficulties in reading the code and knowing what each piece does is that large amounts of code are only used in the developing embryo. For example, the instructions to help form the eye will only be triggered in some cells in an embryo at one critical point in development. For the rest of the period, from egg fertilisation to death of the animal, that strip of code is locked away, turned off or inactive. The secrets of these areas of code are perhaps the most fascinating parts of life itself.

Why does the human hand usually produce five fingers and not six? Which set of genes tells fingers to produce nails on the top and not along the bottom? Could a human have four sets of arms and two pairs of hands? Occasionally, drugs given during pregnancy produce such events—usually because cells become confused as to where they are rather than because of direct genetic damage.

Human embryos going spare

Scientists are busy altering genetic code in fertilised eggs and watching to see what happens to the embryos. In drosophila insects the genes have been identified for early body formation, and adult skin production.[120] We can expect similar progress in mice and monkeys. It will be very tempting for some to try the same with surplus fertilised human eggs resulting from fertility treatments. Many of these techniques involve giving a special drug to a woman, stimulating her ovaries to produce up to twenty eggs instead of only one. These are then removed in a minor operation.

In many centres, all are then exposed to sperm and observed under the microscope to see if they are dividing (ie successfully fertilised). Some eggs (two to three) are then implanted in the womb in the hope that at least one will implant successfully. Quite often none do, although sometimes several succeed, and the result is non-identical twins or triplets. The big ethical question is what to do with the spare embryos, which can be frozen indefinitely. Some may be used in the future to give the mother a chance of having more children without another operation. However, many are being used in experiments, most of which involve allowing them to grow and develop in the laboratory. As we will see in later chapters, this has caused great debate resulting in the creation of the Human Fertilisation and Embryology Authority.

Few limits to the weird and bizarre

At this point you may like to pause to consider for yourself some of the more bizarre possibilities: an animal with the flesh of a cow, the milk of a human mother, the wool of a lamb, the tolerant digestive system of a pig.[121] What about a horse with the efficient gut of a cow, a sheep with the hardiness of a goat, ultra-fast growing trees, bananas from bushes, slower-aging humans? You could think about designing a species of your own with an appropriate name to match.[122]

This may all seem rather far-fetched to you. Even as long ago as 1987 (light years ago in bioengineering progress), it was reported that artificial chromosomes were being manufactured for yeast cells, with claims that production of entire chromosomes for more complex organisms would be possible in the near future.[123]

I leave the final word here to a well-known writer: 'If human blood cells can grow outside the human body, why not human bone cells, muscle cells and nerve cells? And eventually all of them together functioning as a single living organism.' These words were written by Mary Shelley long ago in her novel *Frankenstein: A Modern Protheus*. However, the thought has recurred.[124]

Having looked at some of the astounding progress made in understanding how life works and in designing new species, we can now turn to the High Street supermarket and see what new foods we are likely to be offered in the future. New tomatoes, potatoes, cereals, apples, mushrooms, as well as new kinds of meat, poultry and fish are on the way—but will you recognise them when you see them? In fact you have almost certainly eaten your first genetically altered food, sold as part of a loaf of bread.

5
Strange New Foods

Farming is a high-risk business

The genetic engineer is already making huge changes to the way farmers are growing food, and to what you are eating. You have almost certainly eaten such food already, part of which was made by gene modification—and it had no label on it to tell you. Britain was the first country in the world to approve genetically engineered food for sale in the supermarket. The decision was made quietly, without public debate, and the food (bread made with genetically modified yeast) has been on sale throughout the UK since 1990.[125] We will be looking at the important issues of labelling and consumer safety in a later chapter.

Farming has never been riskier or more competitive than today. In many countries food production is artificially stimulated or destroyed by large fluctuations in market prices. Some of these fluctuations are natural, due to variations in crop yields from year to year, for example. Others are due to systematic rigging of the markets through governments guaranteeing minimum prices.

These steps were designed to prevent the boom-and-bust effect from year to year and to guarantee regular farming income. However, they have led to situations where at a time of mass starvation in Africa, farmers are paid to produce more non-transportable food than we need (milk, butter and beef, for example). As a reaction to this appalling situation, European farmers are now being paid not to farm their land at all—maybe to plant trees instead.

Surplus and famine

Dumping subsidised food onto the world market (during famine, dumping free food is often relabelled as 'aid') also has massive effects on small two-thirds world farmers who can find the value of their produce disappears overnight.

For a Western farmer high yield for low cost is always the key factor: more crops per acre, lower seed cost, lower wastage from disease, greater resistance to frost, heat and drought, quicker ripening time, and less need for fertilisers or pesticides. A 5–10% increase in yield can make all the difference between catastrophic loss and a reasonable return. Farmers are now being promised new cereals, new vegetables and fruits, new animals, new food-producing bacteria and new fungi.

New cereals being made

So what can the genetic engineer offer the farmer? Large manufacturers of pesticides and fertilisers and seed suppliers might look at it all another way. What could the genetic engineers of a rival company come up with that might damage sales?

Four huge areas lie waiting for the farmer of cereal crops:

1. Better seed—greater yield
2. Lower need for fertilisers
3. Lower need for pesticides
4. Biological warfare against pests

At least twenty-seven of the world's largest chemical companies are locked in a fierce battle to produce superior genetically modified cereals with which they can beat their competitors. They know it could be a fight to the death, with many companies being wiped out, unless they can keep up with the pace of new product development in this and related areas, requiring huge amounts of capital investment. As long ago as 1985 a company in the USA successfully took out a patent on one of the first newly 'invented' cereals: this was to protect the creation of a new type of maize with high cell content of a substance called tryptophan.[126]

Lower need for fertilisers

Taking the issue of fertilisers first: there are some bacteria which take nitrogen out of the atmosphere—it is the major gas we breathe—and turn it into nitrates which are the chemicals plants use to grow. Nitrates are needed to form amino acids, used as building blocks in making proteins (see pages 37 and 40). Nitrates are artificially applied in fertilisers.

Some plants such as peas and beans (legumes) have self-fertilising factories in nodules attached to their roots. They create homes for these special bacteria which produce nitrates just where nitrates are needed most: at the roots of the plants. These plants tend to leave more nitrates in the soil at the end of the year than there were at the beginning. So much so, in fact, that before the widespread use of fertilisers, farmers would often sow one of these types of plants into each field roughly every third year to restore the exhausted soil.

Self-fertilising cereals

The farmer's dream would be to take the genetic code for these roots and add them to the genetic code of cereals. Attempts are currently under way to do this. If successful, the turnover of many large chemical companies would be damaged overnight, which is why so many are expecting to switch production from chemical fertilisers to genetically engineered products soon.

Insecticides and pesticides

A further dream would be to grow crops containing their own fungicides, pesticides and insecticides—substances made inside the cells of each plant instead of being absorbed artificially through spraying.[127] Clearly these substances would need to be non-toxic to humans or at least not find their way through the sap into the harvested seed. The dream is becoming reality with viruses already modified to infect and transform plants, giving them insect and disease resistance and weedkiller (herbicide) tolerance.[128] Such steps could also have alarming implications for pesticide manufacturers, but could actually increase sales of weedkiller.

It is interesting that one company (Calgene) is now marketing a new genetically engineered seed which gives resistance to damage from a powerful applied weedkiller—it just happens to be specific protection to the weedkiller produced by the same company. Wheat has now been successfully reprogrammed with herbicide resistance, with vast potential for new strains with drought resistance, ability to grow in salty soils, resistance to fungal attack, and with higher protein content.[129]

Similar work has been carried out by Monsanto, producing crops resistant to glyphosate. The first genetically modified organism to be released in Denmark was a new sugar beet resistant to a herbicide.[130] These new products often guarantee sale of expensive super-seed and own-brand chemicals. Similar work is continuing on cotton, tomatoes, rape seed, potatoes and sugar beet.[131]

At first, 'green' consumers may be misled into thinking that new crops grown without pesticides or fertilisers are more ecologically sound. However, they may soon be wondering what the side-effects are of eating vegetables or other crops programmed to fill themselves with home-made poisons.

Another example of recent progress has been the creation of ninety new kinds of potatoes, each of which has a new gene added to kill off the Colorado beetle. The gene has been taken from a soil-dwelling bacterium which produces a toxin lethal to the beetles. The modified potatoes produce the poison inside their own cells. The taste and appearance are identical in every way to normal potatoes, but is this insecticide safe for humans to eat every day for decades?[132]

At the moment, as we shall see in Chapter 9, there are inadequate controls to protect consumers from such crops. If the substances are produced within a plant, then the plant may be deemed as safe and as wholesome as its original ancestor. Even if the plant is considered unsafe, since it is outwardly identical it will be impossible to prevent wide distribution through Covent Garden and other markets.

No labels on foods

Even if the manufacturers of the new food type volunteer to have it officially approved, there does not have to be any labelling of the product, so consumers will be none the wiser. As we will see later, labelling is also entirely voluntary at the moment. Safety testing is being carried out,[133] but in almost every country of the world there is no proper regulatory authority for genetically created foods. These are all important concerns we will be returning to later.

Most of us have probably already eaten our first genetically engineered food without even knowing it—after all, it is hardly something shops want to shout about, and manufacturers are keeping a very low profile for the same reasons. It could be the quickest way to kill sales by causing anxiety in shoppers in our supermarkets.

Rapid production of new seed

Genetic engineering also allows us to produce new strains of seed more quickly. Usually a single cross-bred cereal plant has to be bred from seed through several generations over several years to produce enough seed to sell and be able to produce more.

Incidentally, there are huge commercial advantages to selling genetically engineered seed with higher yield but sterile seed. In other words the farmer, having lost the need to buy pesticides and fertilisers, now has to buy new seed at inflated prices each year, where previously he or she would have kept some of the harvest back for next year's sowing.

Here is the simple answer to raising millions of seeds from just one genetically engineered plant in just twelve months: plant cloning. Hundreds or even thousands of identical growing plants can be made from just one original. The result is fields ready for harvesting by summer, to produce a massive crop of commercial seed for sale the following year. Plant cloning is of course a well-established practice. A type of plant cloning is taking cuttings and transplanting them. This has been a standard procedure commercially for decades.

Spraying crops with viruses

Progress is also being made in designing new plants which are virus-resistant.[134] Another option for the farmer is to use germ warfare against insects which eat his crops. Research is going on to develop insect viruses which can either be sprayed onto crops or which will be released into the sap by plant cells. In one experiment, a new insect virus was developed. This was tested out on silkworm larvae which caused a lethal overdose of a particular natural insect hormone to be produced by the silkworms. The new virus was 20% more lethal than the original.[135] The silkworms are to caterpillar research what guinea pigs are to human research.

Other types of laboratory-made viruses have also been developed recently by using genetic code for poisons produced by bacteria and inserting it into viruses. The end result has been the same as in silkworms, with the insect larvae infected beginning to produce minute doses of the insecticide themselves in their own body cells.[136]

Cabbage-eating caterpillars have been the targets of new research in Oxford, where scientists have added the gene responsible for scorpion venom to caterpillar viruses. The viruses were to be sprayed onto a cabbage patch as an experiment in 1991. The venom genes contained in the viruses become part of the caterpillars, producing a toxin which immediately paralyses the caterpillars and causes death in a few days.[137]

Could the viruses infect other creatures, causing unexpected problems? All this has profound implications for human safety. Do we want to eat genetically engineered plant or caterpillar viruses with our fresh salad? We will be looking later at existing regulations and whether they are adequate.

New fruit and vegetables

If we turn from cereals to vegetables we find genetic engineers have already left their mark. Unlike cereals which have a long shelf-life when dried, vegetables quickly decay due to their high water content. Many vegetables are also soft and susceptible to bruising, especially if ripe. Farmers are faced with a stark choice: either to harvest unripe crop and hope it softens in the supermarket, or to harvest it ripe—heavier and better quality— but with a risk of severe damage by the time it reaches the wholesalers.

New tomatoes, apples and mushrooms

The tomato is a high value vegetable (some would say it is a fruit) that has been studied carefully by genetic engineers. Small adjustments have been made to produce a 'non-bruising' tomato. The softening gene has been turned off in the plant. It looks good, survives travel well, but some say its taste is strange or inferior. The company ICI recently signed deals with several biotechnology companies in California to develop non-squashy tomatoes, expecting to begin trials in southern Europe in 1993.[138] Recent advertisements in Sunday newspapers in the UK were promoting another genetically engineered strain of tomato bush, guaranteed to grow without support in any soil, producing huge tomatoes up to twelve to fifteen inches in circumference.

Horticulture Research International is a British company making big strides forward in this area. In 1986 the company bred a new apple called Fiesta. They are now working on genetic markers which will tell them when the new genes for pest and disease resistance have successfully 'taken'. They are still at the stage of planting trees and waiting for an orchard to develop over a number of years. The company has also produced a new type of mushroom with better storage qualities and double the shelf-life after harvest.

The company was funded by the government, but this has stopped now that commercially viable products are resulting. The government now expects industry to provide ongoing investment. The British horticultural industry is providing £2.5 million of finance over the next two years.[139] New melons are also being developed in Reading, which will ripen better on supermarket shelves, and new peas have been produced as sources of 'designer starch' for industry.[140]

African exports and strawberries

There are some foods that we will never see in the West unless genetic engineering provides some answers. Only visitors to the tropics know what bananas are supposed to taste like. Supermarket bananas have been picked very early when they are small and have a low sugar content. Locally picked ripe bananas taste like supermarket ones mashed up with brown demerara sugar. There are other kinds of bananas in Africa that do not even survive air travel well. These will never be eaten in quantity abroad—without a genetic refit.

The strawberry is another obvious target for genetic changes as a high-value-for-weight food. The farmer is faced either with going for good taste but lower yield, or high yield with poor flavour and all the same problems about ripeness and bruising. Perhaps gene changes could result in a high yield, good flavour, non-bruising variety.

New or altered animals

Genetic engineering has much to offer farmers looking for higher animal yields—of meat or milk, for example. There does not need to be a change in the genetic code of the animal itself: we can use genetically engineered bacteria to produce hormones to drive the bodies of animals as hard as they can go for maximum profit. This is a similar approach to using insulin as a genetically engineered medicine in humans.

One example of such an application has resulted from the discovery of the genetic code for growth hormone in chickens. This could soon be used to produce marketable chickens faster.[141] Other experiments on chickens are using viruses to program germ cells, with the aim of producing chicks which hatch out with a built-in resistance to chicken viral disease.[142]

Growth hormones drive cows harder

The company Monsanto has just applied to the European Commission for a licence to use a genetically engineered drug on cows called bovine somatotrophin.[143] This artificially stimulates extra milk production producing the same yield with

30% fewer cattle.[144] The Commission has approved the drug use, but the Council for Veterinary Medicinal Products has not yet reached a verdict. In the meantime a temporary ban was applied in the European Community while it considered a whole range of similar biotechnology products.[145]

However, despite the great debates, milk from cows treated with genetically produced bovine growth hormone has been drunk by the British public since 1986—from ten test farms.[146] In 1988 surveys showed that 83% of the general public were opposed to using the product.[147] Even some farmers are opposed to this farming method because they fear bankruptcy if the price of milk falls as a result, while environmentalists also question the need for it when Europe already overproduces milk. As we saw earlier, farmers are already being encouraged with financial incentives to take land out of farm production because it is cheaper than caring for butter mountains.

Protecting cows and humans

In early 1991 the British Veterinary Product Committee recommended that the British government should refuse a licence to the two companies wanting to market the drug. The grounds for objection were not risks to humans or the environment, but concern for the welfare of the overstimulated animals. The hormone does increase the incidence of udder infection (mastitis) and the treatment involves giving cows painful injections. However, other scientists in the USA also query human safety—small amounts of an insulin-like substance seem to be secreted into the milk of treated cows. Some are also concerned about a possible new milk allergy in humans as a result.

In November 1990 new evidence was emerging of other problems, possibly including increased miscarriages in pregnant cows being treated. These new findings have led the USA Food and Drugs Administration (FDA) to say that the drug is unlikely to be licensed for use in the USA 'for some time'.[148] With a ban already announced by German Parliament, the strength of the 'caution' lobby is growing. Meanwhile, in the USA alone, four companies hope to market the drug and have already spent hundreds of millions of dollars in research and development.[149]

New 'super-animals'

We can also use genetic engineering to produce vaccines against animal diseases such as foot and mouth disease.[150] However, as we have already seen, the biggest stakes of all are in genetically engineered farm animals or 'super-animals'. As we shall see later, the sex of embryos can be determined using genetic techniques,[151] and as we have seen already, a whole new herd can be created in months by cloning, but how about genetically altering the first animal before we begin?[152]

In 1987 a scientific paper said that 'within the foreseeable future it will be possible to add foreign genes to the genetic composition of animals in order to transfer disease resistance, rapid growth, fertility and efficient use of foodstuffs to their offspring'. In 1991 at least 62,000 transgenic animals were born in British laboratories alone.[153]

The reality is that the traditional image of a cow as 'Daisy' is totally at odds with what is happening to the modern cow: 'genetically engineered to be a high performance machine, as highly tuned as a racing car . . . and like a car that's pushed flat out . . . it goes bust more easily'.[154]

Patent protection (see pages 62–64) has been available on newly-created animals as well as plants under USA law since an historic decision by the USA supreme court in 1987.[155] The test case involved polypoid oysters. In fact the first gene transfers in mammals happened in mice as long ago as 1976.[156] Since then a large number of animals have been reprogrammed.[157]

Food fads come and go. Doctors are still unable to agree about the relationship between high levels of animal fat in the diet and heart disease. As we will see later, what seems most likely is that a small proportion of the population is sensitive to the damaging effect of animal fats, while for the rest of us the advice is probably irrelevant. We can probably detect who needs to be on low-fat diets through family history of heart disease or strokes, by testing blood cholesterol levels—and in the future by inspecting the genetic code, because such sensitivity seems to be inherited.

Low-fat pigs

However, the public perception of the dangers in eating animal fats is now firmly rooted, and the demand for low-fat meat is therefore growing. In 1987 a new kind of 'transgenic' pig was created for the first time with lower than normal body fat.[158] Fertilised eggs from pigs were injected with a strip of genetic code formed from two fragments, one from a human with the instructions to produce human growth hormone, and the other from a mouse with instructions to activate the gene.

Once injected, the cells were returned to the sow's womb to develop. Out of 341 pigs that resulted, thirty-one were reprogrammed.[159] They developed as mutants, containing pig, mouse and human genetic code—let us call them humigs. The human growth hormone production in the animals lowered body fat and stimulated mammary development (milk production). Moreover, the new animals gave birth to identical offspring five out of six times.

Low-fat sheep

The same experiments were also repeated using fertilised eggs from sheep, but with less success—only three of 111 lambs born were a new creation. However, as long as you can reproduce from the new stock, you only need to have a one in thousand success rate or less to make the effort worthwhile. After all, how much will a company pay for the first of a new superbreed of cow, likely to become a new world-class breed?

Other methods of reprogramming fertilised eggs include infecting them with genetically engineered viruses.[160] This is fast becoming a standard technique. An alternative is to reprogram sperm cells using liposomes (bags of protein containing enzymes and genetic material) and then use the altered sperm to program unfertilised eggs.[161]

A new animal every day

A simpler and easier way to make new animals is to remove a cell from an embryo at a very early stage, reprogram it using any one of many standard methods, and then replace it into the embryo. These primitive embryonic stem cells (ES cells) go on growing and contribute to every structure of the animal in the future. The result is a hybrid: every organ will contain some altered cells and some originals.[162]

Technology allows the generation of large numbers of slightly different animals with extremely precise genetic changes. As a result we should be able to test tens of thousands of randomly selected fragments of genetic code in embryos to see what the effects are.[163] We need little or no understanding of the code inserted. Any improvements on nature that result can be preserved for ever in a new species by cloning or natural reproduction.

Cow udders as medicine factories

The demand is also rising for skimmed milk. What do you do with all the cream when you cannot sell it as cream or butter? The udders of cows have been particular targets for the genetic engineer: here is a massive chemical factory producing very large amounts of complex proteins.

We can either try to adjust the composition and flavour of the milk in some way, or program the udders to manufacture completely new substances which we can later extract from the milk to use as medicines.[164] Such milk would be unlikely to be suitable for drinking, even after extraction of the medicine.

Human breast milk from cows

Mothers are also being increasingly driven back to old-fashioned breast feeding of their babies as more and more evidence grows of the long-term damage to some through early feeding on cows' milk—even in modified powder form.

A first immediate challenge has been to reprogram the udders of a cow by inserting the human genes a mother's breast cells use to make the special formula for human breast milk. This has been done in cow embryos and the reprogrammed cows are now growing up fast. We can expect to see human breast milk substitute from cows in the not-too-distant future. The next problem is to alter the metabolism of cows, as we have with pigs, to produce animals which grow more flesh faster and less bone or fat.[165]

Frozen embryos sexed and screened

A genetic engineering company called Granada Genetics in Texas said recently:

> The concept of producing large numbers of genetically identical embryos, frozen, sexed, screened for economic traits and produced inexpensively from slaughterhouse by-products is within our grasp . . . all . . . have already been demonstrated. What will happen to protein production when commercial cow herds can be made up of one or two female clone lines mated to bulls of the same clone? The obvious answer is predictability of performance to a magnitude never before achieved in agriculture.[166]

Rapid progress is being made. It is even possible that we may see new animals being sold in meat markets, although one suspects consumer pressure will mean they will still be called by familiar names to avoid anxieties being raised. Would you buy geep meat (combined goat and sheep) at 40p a pound less than lamb? Sheep have already been modified, although not as dramatically as this yet.[167]

Mousey trout and strange rabbits

New types of transgenic fish are also being made. Rainbow trout have been reprogrammed by taking fertilised eggs and adding a second copy of the gene for Rainbow trout growth hormone attached to a mouse gene designed to activate it artificially. In 1990, of 3,104 eggs treated in this way, 25% (783) hatched, out of which 4% were of the new form. Of 180 hatchlings, thirty-five survived as adult fish. Two were of the new type. The new fish also gave rise to offspring with the same genetic characteristics.[168] The list of transformed creatures is long—even rabbits have been changed.[169]

Once a transgenic animal has been made, very large numbers of others can be created by cloning—well established, as we have seen, for duplicating sheep and cattle embryos. These are produced by separating cells at the earliest stage after fertilisation (see page 49). However, nuclear transplantation will open the way for cloning on a much larger scale.[170]

Drastic changes in livestock breeding

The Department of Meat and Animal Science at Wisconsin University in the USA published a paper in 1990 which said:

> Efficient in vitro systems for maturing oocytes and capacitating spermatozoa, for fertilising and developing the embryos have resulted in commercial . . . production of embryos. Cloning of embryos by nuclear transfer has been accomplished for sheep, cattle, pigs, and rabbits, with nuclear material supplied by embryos as late as the 120 cell stage in sheep. Embryos have been recloned . . . Research is needed . . . so that the number of clones may be increased to thousands or millions.
>
> Transgenic embryos or offspring have been produced for mice, rats, rabbits, chickens, fish, sheep, pigs and cattle . . . badly needed efforts to map the genome of domestic animals. These and other new technologies promise to change livestock breeding drastically over the next decade.[171]

Cloning monsters by mistake

However, cloning is not without its risks. Scientists in Cambridge were horrified recently when attempts to mass produce herds of cloned identical animals went disastrously wrong. Calves which should have weighed only 80lb at birth were developing to massive 150lb monsters.[172] The same laboratory that announced the birth of the first geep (half goat and half sheep) placed cloned embryos inside 1,000 cows. They were unsaleable after the discovery that one in five was too large and one in twenty was a massive giant. The animals end up not much larger than usual as adults.

This strange phenomenon has been called one of the most important discoveries in developmental biology in the last ten years. Mistreatment of these embryos is causing them to grow in this strange way. The problem has highlighted our lack of understanding. In the meantime, the Milk Marketing Board which has financed the research continues to justify the work in order to produce cows with standard characteristics and milk composition—'scientists don't know what is going to happen until they do it'.[173]

However, there are alternatives to using animals for food at all.

Food from microbes

Even if you are not a vegetarian or vegan by conscience or personal taste, there is a fundamental problem in growing animals for food. The trouble with animals is that they are inefficient: almost everything a cow eats is turned into heat keeping warm, energy in moving around, and cells for tissues wearing out, such as gut lining shed into cow dung, or to make skin and hair. Some undigested food is also excreted as dung, although cows are much more efficient than horses which excrete huge amounts of undigested cellulose in food.

However, even plants are not always as efficient as you might think in trapping solar energy and using the power to make proteins, sugars or fibre. Basically all we eat is solar powered directly or indirectly. The solar energy is stored, converted or transferred in one way or another. How about using another form of stored energy to fuel human beings with good food for us to burn inside our bodies?

Nuclear power for food

Bacteria already exist which eat oil and grow to produce protein which we could use as food. What about bacteria that burn hydrogen to produce energy? Nuclear power or hydroelectric power can be used to make electricity. Electricity can be used to turn water into oxygen and hydrogen—the same chemical reaction that happens when car batteries are recharged. Hydrogen can be fed to bacteria which use it as fuel to grow. There is then a potential way of producing food from nuclear power.

Here is a summary of a long process:

(a) Nuclear reaction—heat—boils water—steam—drives turbine—generates electricity.

(b) Electric current passes through chemicals in water, in a container like a massive car battery—hydrogen gas and oxygen gas bubble to the surface—hydrogen collected and pumped to large flask containing growing bacteria.

(c) Special bacteria use up hydrogen and oxygen—energy from the gases converted in bacteria to energy in cells—cells grow and divide.

(d) Thick sludge of cells harvested—sludge processed to form food—food sold in supermarket.

Because energy itself is likely to continue to be at a premium, we will probably find our best results will continue to come from new plants producing most of our dietary needs from sunlight and soil, rather than through bacteria directly or through the unnecessary wasteful intermediary of a farm animal.

Progress on plant texture and taste is also needed before we will all be converted to being vegetarians. In the meantime, yeasts are also being genetically engineered as future food sources.[174] When the world's oil supplies have nearly run out—less than a generation away—there will be a huge need to produce low-cost alternatives to petrol for cars. One well-proven alternative is ethanol or alcohol. New ways are being tried to program E. coli bacteria to produce ethanol.[175]

Fast-growing trees for timber and oxygen

One of the greatest challenges for humans is how to grow trees fast. We can build a fifty-storey office block in fifty weeks, but a large tree takes over 200 years to grow and is impossible to move without damage. A new forest planted today will take a generation to produce real benefits, whether in terms of quality timber or oxygen production. Trees like the Japanese bamboo grow over a metre a day. Perhaps gene changes in the future will allow us to produce instant forests taking only ten years to become established instead of thirty to fifty. We would need to be sure the trees were non-seeding, and died when cut down, or they could become a terrible ecological menace, taking over all natural woodlands as well as other land.

Having considered some of the range of ways genetic engineering is having an impact on what we grow and what we eat, we now need to look at the most important area of all: genetic engineering for maximum health, using genes in medicine.

6

Doctors Using Genes

Gene discoveries are beginning to revolutionise medical[176] and surgical practice.[177] However, as soon as we put gene technology and medicine together we need to make a big distinction between techniques to identify and abort foetuses on the basis of their genetic code (eg, Down's babies) and techniques designed to produce cures or treatments.

Prevention or destruction?

Although at first glance it appears that embryo research is assisting in the prevention of many inherited diseases, this is only being achieved by encouraging mothers to have abortions if doctors suspect that the developing child may have a gene problem. This is 'prevention by destruction' or 'birth denial' rather than prevention through counselling, education, treatment or cure.

Our growing understanding of the human genome means that a vastly increased range of predictions can be made about what an embryo will turn out to be like. In the past, such genetic tests were confined to gross problems like Down's Syndrome, where an entire chromosome has been added to the basic number of forty-six. This defect is obvious when looking down an ordinary light microscope using special techniques.

Incidentally, taking a sample from a developing foetus, or

from the fluid surrounding it, is not without its hazards. Spontaneous miscarriage can follow, so it is a procedure to be considered very carefully—whatever someone's position on abortion—especially where the mother is in her late thirties or early forties and the couple have taken some years to conceive. In this situation it is a particular tragedy to discover after a doctor-induced miscarriage that the dead baby was completely normal. It may be the only pregnancy the woman will ever have.[178] Some techniques, such as ultrasound, can detect a number of structural abnormalities without such risk.

Screening for bowel cancer

An example of the rapid extension of pre-natal screening is for the inherited polyposis gene which gives rise to bowel cancer at an early age. One case was reported recently in London of a young woman whose bowel was checked for early cancer when she was a teenager because her father had died from the disease aged thirty-eight.[179] Tell-tale signs of early changes were found. Almost all her large bowel was removed in an operation which will almost guarantee her freedom from the cancer. The small part remaining is close to the end of the gut and can be easily checked.

Although young she had more or less decided to be sterilised to prevent any risk of passing on the defective gene to her children. She was referred to a genetic counsellor who informed her that although the precise polyposis gene had not yet been found, specific markers near it had been located, allowing the rogue gene to be identified correctly in nine out of ten of those carrying it. The normal gene acts as a brake on cell division. If the gene is defective, bowel cells tend to grow faster than they should and a cancer forms.

She then became pregnant and her foetus was tested at ten weeks.[180] Although in 1990 we only knew the general location of the gene and could only detect it through a marker gene nearby, now the gene itself has been precisely located and identified. The gene tells colon cells to make a regulatory protein, so testing protein levels could be a way to diagnose the polyposis gene in the future. By manufacturing the protein genetically and using it as a medicine we may also be able to develop a new treatment.[181] We may also be able to reprogram colon cells back to normal.

Cystic fibrosis guarantees

This kind of work is often not brought to public attention until some time afterwards so that only properly checked results are published. However, big news is hard to keep quiet, as doctors at the Hammersmith Hospital in London found recently when the press discovered a baby had been born with a built-in 'genetic guarantee' not to develop cystic fibrosis in the future.

Both parents carried the defective gene and their first child had developed the disease, with chronic chest infections and problems absorbing food. The gene was first isolated in August 1989. Sperm and eggs were taken from the parents and fertilisation took place in the laboratory. Developing embryos were checked for the defective gene, and a 'healthy' embryo was inserted.[182] Without such intervention the parents were faced with a one in four chance that their second child would also have the disease—unless they wished to test the developing child some way into pregnancy and proceed with an abortion if the result was positive.

Incidentally, I often wonder about the conflict between the view of many that all mothers should have the right to a healthy child, and the right of a child with medical problems to be born—whatever the religious or philosophical persuasions of the parents. In any event, no guarantee of normality can ever be given—there will always be an element of uncertainty. These are difficult and controversial areas which we will return to in Chapter 10.

The Elephant Man gene

A large number of other genes are being pinpointed with new discoveries almost every month. One recent discovery has been the genes causing neurofibromatosis, which at its most extreme produced the famous Elephant Man. The genes affect one in 3,000 of all babies born, the great majority of which are only mildly affected. The genes cause symptoms ranging from brown patches on the skin ('café au lait') to multiple benign tumours arising from the sheaths of nerves.[183]

Breast cancer from a gene

Another example is in understanding breast cancer, which kills 15,000 women a year—the commonest cancer in women, with 5–10% of all cases likely to be due to a faulty gene. Women with a mother and a sister with breast cancer have more than eight times the risk of developing it themselves. Women with relatives who have developed breast cancer after the menopause have only a slightly increased risk. It is the younger women with breast cancer where genes seem to be most important. Cancer of the ovary is another tumour which appears to have an important inherited component.

A laboratory in Hertfordshire believes it has located two faulty genes on chromosome seventeen—a chromosome already highlighted as suspect by American researchers.[184] Researchers are very close to finding genetic markers so that high risk of breast cancer can be detected in the womb or after birth. These so-called oncogenes are found in a number of cancers, although we do not yet understand fully how they work. Since they control cell growth they may play an important role in normal cell regulation.

Mental handicap genes

Progress has been so fast that we are now well past the peak for discovering new medically important genes. A recent addition to the list, as we saw in an earlier chapter, has been the discovery of the fragile X gene which causes mental handicap.[185]

Having worked with some people who have had severe disabilities from birth, I am very uneasy about the judgements of the non-disabled or 'healthy' on the quality of life of all others. It is true that someone, say, born blind or with a likelihood of future disease, might be so depressed later on as to commit suicide, but it is also true that the great majority of those who are visually impaired, or who experience serious chronic illness, nevertheless lead full, active, independent and fulfilling lives.

Indeed the main handicap (if there is one) can be that society is still very unthinking when it comes to design and the way things are done. One or two wheelchair ramps seems to just about sum up the response of many larger organisations to the needs of the disabled. Are we carrying out pre-birth destruction of future people because we cannot tolerate wheelchairs or braille signs in the lifts? Professor Stephen Hawking, the world-famous cosmologist in Cambridge, is a well-known example of the supreme triumph of many over severe physical disability.

Prophesying illness

The whole area of genetic screening is likely to become very complex in the future. Although there are a large number of genetic diseases, they are still quite unusual—only two in a hundred of those ill today are needing care purely because of a gene problem.[186] The commonest killers of all are caused by a number of complex factors operating together, of which just one is genetic.

Doctors have known this for a great many years, which is why family history is so important. Doctors in hospital will often ask if your parents are still alive and, if not, what they died from. An example is heart disease: a man whose grandfather and father both died before the age of sixty from heart attacks is at higher risk of developing diseased coronary arteries than someone whose parents lived until they were in their nineties. The geneticist should be able to help us confirm who in the general population is likely to become ill from particular diseases.[187] This is already the case for specific diseases such as Huntington's chorea.

For over ten years we have been able to predict risk of many illnesses by using a marker in cell walls called HLA antigen, which is produced by chromosome number six. The most accurate prophecies are about ankylosing spondylitis, a deformity of the spine causing the bones in the back to fuse together. The HLA-B27 type is present in 95% of those with the condition, and one in sixteen with HLA-B27 develop the disease. Illnesses which can be linked to HLA antigens include asthma, hay fever, high blood pressure, heart attacks, depression, diabetes, acute appendicitis, glandular fever, cancers and multiple sclerosis.[188] It has even been suggested that HLA antigen types may affect how rapidly people develop AIDS after infection with HIV.[189]

Who needs a low-fat diet?

For the last ten years we have recognised that if 10,000 adults eat a diet high in animal fats—especially cholesterol—then the number with heart disease is likely to rise. The huge marketing campaigns by margarine manufacturers have been built on this fact, but some experts now think that for the great majority of the population, fat intake is probably irrelevant. However, fat intake may be very important indeed for a minority with a genetic problem where animal fats in the diet tend to produce damaging changes in the body.

A simple test, taking a couple of hours, could help us find out which group we are in—saving dietary inconvenience, expense and enlarging food choice. Such genetically influenced diseases affect at least one in ten of the population, and include diabetes mellitus, certain types of cancers, heart disease and strokes.[190]

Gene cures and treatments

Gene cures or treatments are an area of immense activity and fall into several groups:

1. Programming bacteria, fungi or mammalian cells to produce missing hormones or other substances including complex chemicals. This has been recognised as an area of major importance for many years.[191]

2. Growing white cells (soldier cells used to fight infection)

to harvest special 'monoclonal antibodies' designed to attack things like cancers. This is a form of human cloning.

3. Growing skin, bone marrow or other cells as a form of cloning of tissues.

4. Producing vaccines.

5. Reprogramming human cells—for example to cure HIV infection and AIDS.

6. Reprogramming genes in an embryo to cure genetic diseases.

1. Program cell factories

The trouble with so many recent discoveries about how the body works is that we keep discovering more and more complex chemical substances and special structures. Although we understand an enormous amount about what they do and how presence or lack produces disease, they are so complicated that we cannot make them in a chemistry laboratory. As we have seen (page 34), a laboratory the size of a tower block would be needed to make large amounts of some of these things. It would be very expensive, slow and unreliable.

However, similar chemical reactions and assembly lines operate in almost every living cell. We have looked earlier at the possibility of hijacking the factories inside cells and getting them to do the work.[192] The result could be a small production unit maybe in two or three large rooms containing large stainless steel barrels of cells. These could produce enough of, say, a hormone to treat several thousand people. Hundreds of experiments have been going on for some years to refine this technology.[193] Bacteria from the gut are now being used quite routinely in medicine to make all kinds of substances, in ways that would have looked like science fiction just eight years ago.[194]

Gene factory closed by outcry

However, although the benefits may be obvious, such work has also caused great controversy, with at least one large pharmaceutical company in Germany forced to close a £20 million plant for genetically engineered insulin production[210] following a legal

Fig 11: Genetically engineered drugs

The first thirteen genetically engineered drugs to be marketed commercially

Product	Originator	Year	Indication
Insulin (Humulin)	Eli Lilly	1982	Diabetes
Human Growth hormone (Protropin)	Genentech	1985	Growth hormone deficiency in children
2 a-Interferon (Intron A)	Schering-Plough	1985	Hairy cell leukaemia
2 b-Interferon (Roferon-A)	Hoffman-La Roche	1986	Hairy cell leukaemia
Hepatitis B vaccine (Engerix B)	SK & F	1986	Hepatitis B vaccine
Digoxin monoclonal antibody (Digibind)	Wellcome	1986	Digoxin antidote
Orthoclonal OKT3	Cilag	1986	Rejection prophylaxis in kidney transplants
Somatotropin (Humatrope)	Eli Lilly	1987	Growth hormone deficiency in children
tPA (Activase)	Genentech	1987	Myocardial infarction
Erythropoetin (Eprex)	Amgen/Cilag	1988	Anaemia (RBC) particularly in chronic kidney failure
GM-CSF	Amgen	1989	Neutropenia
C-CSF (Neupogen)	Amgen/ Hoffman-La Roche	1990	Neutropenia
Factor 8	Genentech/ Bayer	1991	Haemophilia

challenge by the Green Party.[211] The response may simply be to move production to another country.

Work is also well developed using reprogrammed fungi cells[212] and human cells[213] as factories for medicine production in the laboratory. Insect larvae have also been used: infected by viruses containing human genetic code. The larvae produce large amounts of useful substances: for example about 8–9 mg of pure human adenosine deaminase can be obtained from about twenty larvae.[214] These concentrations are up to 350 times greater than can be obtained from human thymus or leukaemic cells. Complex proteins such as Factor 8 for haemophilia require mammalian cells to be used. Whole mammal bodies such as mice could be used as production units like the insect larvae above[215] as long as the substance is relatively neutral in effect on the producing animal.

100 drug and vaccine trials

Worldwide, scientists are investigating over 250 possible drugs produced by genetic engineering. Over 100 human drugs and vaccines are currently undergoing trials.[216] Some, as we have seen, have been remarkably successful. Erythropoetin has helped patients with kidney failure enormously: kidneys not only clean the blood, but also produce erythropoetin which stimulates the bone marrow to form red blood cells. Until this revolutionary new treatment existed, those needing dialysis were chronically anaemic, and often needed regular blood transfusions.

Bacteria have been used with great success to produce a substance to stimulate white cell production when it has been damaged as a side-effect of cancer chemotherapy. The substance (granulocyte macrophage colony stimulating factor) was discovered and isolated in 1983. A more potent version was isolated a year later and was in full production as a medicine by 1989, manufactured by Amgen.[217]

Treatment for haemophilia

The search for an artificial source of Factor 8 for those with haemophilia has been enormously accelerated by the tragedy

Fig 12: Human substances being made genetically

1. Human epidermal growth factor[195]

2. Human granulocyte colony stimulating factor[196]

3. Human growth hormone[197]

4. Human manganese superoxide dismutase[198]

5. Tissue plasminogen activator[199]

6. Human adenosine deaminase[200]

7. Human purine nucleoside phosphorylase[201]

8. Human hypoxanthine granine phosphoribosyl transferase[202]

9. Human Insulin[203]

10. Human Ferritin[204]

11. Human Fibroblast growth factor[205]

12. Human Calmodulin[206]

13. Human Factor 8[207]

14. Human Factor 9

15. Human Interferon[208]

16. Human Somatogen[209]

(Incomplete list)

caused by accidental HIV infection and AIDS deaths. This followed the use of Factor 8 obtained from plasma in blood donations. As we saw in an earlier chapter, special treatments to eliminate viral contamination only began in 1985, by which time over 1,000 men and 250 children with haemophilia in the UK were already HIV infected.

It was a surprise to many doctors to find that the virus was not only transmitted in the blood, but was also very hardy—surviving freeze drying and storage for several months before injection. Gonorrhoea bacteria would never survive such rough treatment.

Factor 8 is a protein made from 2,332 amino acids (building blocks for proteins—see pages 37 and 41) in a set order. If only one or two of these are incorrectly placed, then the complex shape of the coiled molecule is changed (Fig 5, page 38) and the structure has little or no biological effect on blood clotting. The molecule is too complex to make in the test-tube. We are also unable to grow human liver cells (which normally make Factor 8) in sufficient amounts.

Human Factor 8 from hamster cells

The Factor 8 gene, combined with all the other human genes, had first to be 'decombined' or separated from the rest of the genes in the human cell. Then it was 'recombined' with genes in hamster cells which grow very well in industrial vats. This new Factor 8 is then called 'recombinant'. The final stage involves extracting Factor 8 from the brew. It is then mixed with albumin, a protein in human blood which can be subjected to rigorous processes to destroy viruses before it is used. By July 1990 over 150 people with haemophilia had been successfully treated with genetically engineered Factor 8 in the UK.[218]

Lack of Factor 9 is the cause of another similar bleeding disorder. Although a smaller molecule, it is more complicated to produce. Mice cells have been programmed to produce it, but it is still experimental. However, the biggest aim of all is to cure haemophilia by reprogramming the person's own cells. This is still some way ahead.[219]

Artificial blood from bacteria

Scientists have also made rapid progress in producing an artificial blood substitute using bacteria. Clinical trials have begun in the USA on a synthetic oxygen-carrying molecule very similar to human haemoglobin. The substitute could be on sale in five years and is likely to be marketed by Somatogen.[220] Sales could be worth tens of billions of dollars. It will not replace normal blood altogether, as it is missing all the other substances in blood, including the clotting factors we have looked at above.

Production of antibiotics

Programming of soil micro-organisms such as streptomyces is one way to produce a new generation of antibiotics.[221] Modifying these organisms can produce a wide variety of new substances, each of which can be tested for possible effects on bacteria, either preventing them from growing or interfering with their genes.[222]

2. Monoclonal antibodies

The production of monoclonal antibodies has been one of the most important advances in modern medicine, promising us new weapons to fight cancer and detect disease.[223] However, we first need to understand what antibodies are and exactly how they work.

Apart from the human brain, perhaps the most remarkable part of the body is the immune system which fights infection. Every hour of every day the immune system is fighting infections, although we only realise it if we develop symptoms. There are two major problems. The first is that germs and human cells come in all sorts of shapes and sizes, often looking very similar. Therefore the body needs to take great care to distinguish friend from foe before attacking. Secondly, once a cell has been identified as foreign it needs to be swiftly destroyed.

Killing germs is hard because every germ has a different outside appearance and has to be attacked differently by the body. If white cells are too aggressive they may easily end up fighting and killing normal healthy body cells, thinking they are germs. When this happens we say the person has an auto-immune disease because the body is attacking itself. Such diseases are common and include rheumatoid arthritis, some forms of diabetes, thyroid problems and kidney failure.

Recognising your own body

White cells build up a library of all the cell shapes and sizes in the body before birth, so that all cells, viruses and other foreign material can be checked against the library before ordering an attack. Some cells are missed because soldier cells cannot get to them. The inside of the eye for instance never becomes part of the library. You see the effects if someone has a severe eye injury. If the damaged eye is not removed quickly, the immune system begins to attack it as foreign, and will also start to destroy the other eye as well—a process which cannot easily be stopped once started.

Destroying enemy cells

To protect our own cells from damage when fighting germs, the immune system measures up the wall of the germ and makes antibodies to measure, a precise fit. Almost every germ needs a different shape of antibody. That is why having measles does not protect you from chickenpox, or having flu does not prevent a cold. If germs change their shapes, as cold and influenza viruses do, then the body has to make a brand new set of antibodies to fit each time.

There are tens of thousands of different antibody shapes available. These fit every possible variation in the walls of bacteria, fungi, viruses and other organisms. They can also detect some cancer cells as foreign. Once cells are coated with antibody, their cell walls are either punctured directly, causing the cells to die, or other white cells attach themselves to the antibody-coated cells and kill them.

New cancer treatments

As we have seen earlier, gene research has a huge role to play in the fight against cancer, and monoclonal antibodies are an important part of this.[224] We know antibodies and white cells destroy cancers very well because cancers are so common in people where the immune system is damaged or put to sleep with drugs such as very high dose steroids. Most of us probably develop cancer cells on a regular basis. They are recognised by the body as foreign and destroyed. Sometimes the destruction rate is not fast enough and the cancer keeps growing—even if more slowly than otherwise.

Doctors have been trying to make a 'magic bullet' out of antibodies by taking white cells from a donor and exposing them in a test-tube to cancer cells. Less than one in 10,000 white cells will react: the ones programmed from birth to recognise this particular shape and produce the right fitting antibodies. If these reacting cells are cloned, then huge amounts of specific antibody can be produced to fit this particular tumour.[225] Monoclonal antibodies can be given as a medicine by injection, knowing that the antibody molecules will be carried around the body safely, hopefully not harming any cells at all except the ones they target.

Cloning white cells

Cloning of white cells calls for special techniques:[226] genetic code from cells producing the antibody required is transferred into cancerous myeloma cells. These myeloma cells grow well in the laboratory and once reprogrammed will go on multiplying, producing the specific shaped antibody indefinitely. We can even mix up the genetic code inserted into myeloma cells so, for example, one end of the antibody molecule produced is identical to that in a mouse while the other end is human.[227] Such changes provide a unique set of tools to diagnose and treat illnesses.[228]

There have been some concerns expressed at the use of some kinds of cancerous cells in genetic engineering, especially if the reason they are cancerous is because of infection by a tumour-producing virus. The risks are generally considered to be minimal[229]—less than one in a million, even if viral genetic code were to find its way into a medical preparation as an impurity.[230]

Cancer treatment still experimental

Although antibodies are being used increasingly in cancer treatments[231] and in blood testing or other laboratory procedures, they are still experimental, and results have sometimes been disappointing. The latest work is focusing on adding a poison—or even a little radioactivity—to each antibody molecule so that even if the antibody and other white cells cannot kill the germ directly, they can at least release high doses of poison or of radioactivity right where it is needed.

This whole area is developing very fast and has a huge potential for new treatments in the future.[232] We urgently need such treatments. Up to one in three of the people you know will die of cancer. Treatments that are currently available to kill cancer cells often kill many normal cells as well, which is why side-effects can be so severe.

Diagnostic or laboratory tools

Monoclonal antibodies are turning out to be extraordinarily useful in hundreds of laboratory tests ranging from immunoassays in diagnosis by detection of tiny amounts of different proteins, to imaging of different parts of the body by attaching dyes, markers or radioactive molecules to antibodies.[233] As genetic engineering techniques improve, new doors are being opened.

We already use antibodies against human pregnancy hormones in 'instant' pregnancy tests sold by chemists. We use them also in the test for the AIDS virus (HIV) infection. Whereas we were previously limited to cloning antibody types using strips of previously existing genetic code, we are now able to write the code completely from scratch, with infinitely possible variations.[234] Literally any shaped antibody can now be made—and what is more, be made to look precisely like human antibody so it survives in the body longer.

3. Growing skin, bone marrow or other cells

In a previous chapter we looked at the benefits of cloning skin cells, preferably using skin from the person who needs more. This is usually as a result of massive burns. Most people with severe burns die because burned skin leaks large amounts of fluid. You see this on a small scale if you burn yourself on a saucepan and get a blister. The urgent need is to get a temporary covering of skin. Skin from other humans or even animals may help for the first few days before the immune system attacks and destroys the graft. However, the only long-term replacement is likely to be skin from the same person—or from an identical twin.

New skin for severe burns

The traditional method of covering skin loss from a severe burn is to remove small pieces of skin from elsewhere on the body and cut them up into tiny pieces. These are placed on the healing burn like growing plants which spread until the whole area is covered. Obviously someone who is severely burned is not going to be able to spare enough skin to cover, especially as each donor site becomes another painful wound needing to heal and easily capable of becoming infected. The tiny grafts are themselves very vulnerable to being destroyed by infection.

Growing skin for each individual in the laboratory, from their own cells, is the best solution and one which is now working well. Skin cells can be persuaded to grow into large sheets very quickly— certainly a lot faster than when covering a wound during natural healing.

New bone marrow in leukaemia

Bone marrow cells are ideal for growing in the test-tube because they tend to operate as independent individuals rather than as cells permanently fixed together in an organ like the liver. One of the most drastic forms of cancer treatment is that for acute leukaemia. The stakes are often high because many who have this illness are children or young adults.

Despite the huge side-effects, one method of treatment is to give the entire body a massive dose of radiation. As a result, all the bone marrow cells die. Red blood cells all die in around 100 days, so the person becomes very anaemic, although blood transfusions can help on a short-term basis. The biggest problem however is that in order to kill off the white cells in the body that were cancerous and dividing too fast, we have also killed off all the others, leaving the body completely defenceless against infection.

Bone marrow transplants

It is possible to take a small piece of bone marrow from a donor and transplant it. The cells gradually fill the large bones and go on to make red and white cells as usual. However, you can see that if the match is not perfect, the new donated white cells could decide that the entire body of the sick person is foreign and a massive auto-immune reaction could follow, gradually destroying the body from within.

A way round this has been provided by the genetic engineer—a second revolutionary way will be looked at in the next chapter. If we can find some normal white cells from a sample of diseased bone marrow before we give the radiation, we could grow these in the laboratory, giving back the person's own white cells at the end. Growing them in the test-tube also allows us to be absolutely certain that the cells put back are really healthy. This cloning of bone marrow cells is now quite routine in some places.

Non-stick coating for equipment

Another use of cloned cells is to give a biological surface to pieces of medical equipment made of metal or plastics before they are inserted into the body. This is especially important for tubes carrying blood, to reduce the risk of blood clotting inside the tube. One medical team has successfully reprogrammed cells from the lining of blood vessels in sheep so they produce human anti-clotting substances. They achieved this by inserting the human gene for plasminogen into viruses (retroviruses) which then infected the sheep cells. The cells were then grown in sheets covering the stainless steel tubes before insertion. Results have been excellent.[235]

Repairing the surface of damaged arteries

Progress is also being made in the treatment of blood vessel narrowing caused by arteriosclerosis. Here we find that minor damage to the artery wall causes smooth muscle cells in the wall to start growing and the vessel to close. Genetically altered smooth muscle cells from pig blood vessels have been successfully transplanted and observed to see how they behave. The hope is to develop alternative treatments for vascular disease.[236]

4. Producing vaccines

One of the most complicated of all structures to manufacture artificially is the wall of a bacterium or virus. Creating cell factories to do this enables us to produce very large amounts of germ fragments which are not infectious, but which we can use to prime the immune system so that when the real germ enters, it is rapidly recognised and destroyed.[237]

This is the basis of the widely-used and highly-effective vaccine against hepatitis B virus,[238] the first genetically engineered vaccine to be licensed for medical use,[239] marketed by Smith Kline and French[240] and recommended by the Department of Health for health workers.[241] It is also the basis for development of a new vaccine against whooping cough[242] and for early work on an AIDS vaccine, as we will see in the next chapter.

Smallpox and polio

Another method of vaccination is to use live virus from a different strain that only produces mild symptoms. For such a vaccine to be effective it must have an outer coating which is so similar to the dangerous type that the body will be prepared in future to fight it.

It was Edward Jenner in the last century who noticed during a local epidemic of smallpox that women who were milking cows on the farms never seemed to have the disease. He began to realise that there must be a very similar virus in cows which was producing mild illness in humans, later protecting against smallpox. The cow illness was identified as cowpox and vaccination using cowpox quickly became an established medical practice.

Another well-known example of a live vaccine is the strain of virus used to fight polio. Polio is an 'enteric' virus, spread by viruses in faeces contaminating what goes into the mouth. Once inside the lining of the gut the virus quickly multiplies, releasing more viruses into the blood from which they infect and destroy nerve cells, producing paralysis or even death. In many countries of the world polio has largely become a thing of the past due to vaccination.

Infectious vaccine spreads

With polio vaccination another very interesting thing often happens: because it is a live vaccine (usually given by placing a drop of virus solution on a sugar lump to eat) it multiplies as you would expect in the gut. Large numbers of infectious virus particles are released in the stools of a vaccinated child. Thus if, say, eight out of ten children in a class at school have been vaccinated, the chances are that the other two will 'catch' the same vaccine and the whole class will end up immune.

The lesson from this is that viruses can and do travel, and we had better be very careful indeed before treating people with live viruses. Some would say that the polio virus and its milder variant are highly infectious, unlike many of the synthetic viruses now being used in experimental treatments of various kinds. The big question is whether the stability of synthetic viruses can be guaranteed. Could they change inside the animal or human in some way that we could not have predicted in advance? If changes take place, could the new mutations be dangerous for the carrier or to others?

Viruses can become more dangerous

Scientists recently took two different strains of pseudorabies virus, one of which had been genetically engineered elsewhere, to form the basis of a vaccine. The other strain had been processed in conventional ways (attenuated) to produce milder disease. Both were given to sheep simultaneously.

The result was that sheep cells became muddled as to which virus they were producing. The viral programming and production became jumbled up and hybrids or mutants resulted. A new strain of virus emerged that had never been seen before, and which had the potential for unpredictable and 'undesirable' effects. Those who ran the study at the US Department of Agriculture concluded that there was 'a need for thorough assessment of micro-organisms in the animal environment'.[243]

Animals and humans may be carrying any number of viruses of various types at any time. Therefore some possibility exists of two strains recombining whenever genetically engineered viruses are used. Having said this, the number of times such recombination seems to happen naturally seems to be quite small, although HIV could be one recent example, if we conclude that it arose as a spontaneous mutation of a very similar virus in animals.

A vaccine for malaria

Malaria is a disease affecting the health of millions in the two-thirds world. With rapidly spreading resistance to the main anti-malarial drugs, this blood-borne parasite is becoming more and more difficult to control. It is impossible to eradicate the large Anopheles mosquito, although numbers can be reduced by elimi-nating all obvious breeding sites other than marshes or the edge of lakes. Vaccine development is being greatly accelerated by genetic techniques to help us understand the various forms that the parasite takes and to construct biological weapons against it.[244]

Another group of tropical parasites being investigated genetically are the Kinetoplastids which cause trypanosomiasis and leishmaniasis.[245] Bacteria are also being reprogrammed to produce new vaccines against typhoid and cholera.[246]

5. Reprogramming human cells

In a few years' time doctors may be giving new genes to their patients as routinely as they give antibiotics today.[247] Once we have learned what genetic code is missing or damaged in people with genetic diseases, it opens up the possibility of 'gene replacement therapy'.[248]

Several approaches are being considered, one of which is the subject of the next chapter. The first approach is to inject the relevant gene into the tissue where the abnormality is evident, in the hope that some DNA will find its way into the damaged cells. This is likely to be tried in people with Duchenne Muscular Dystrophy (DMD), a genetic disease affecting boys only, which causes muscle wasting, confining people to wheelchairs at an early age with death usually by the age of twenty.

Injecting genes to treat muscle problems

Boys with DMD inherit a defective gene from their mothers who are not affected. As a result, their bodies are unable to make a substance called dystrophin. The gene was first isolated in the USA in 1986 and turned out to be very large (a related gene causing the more common Myotonic Dystrophy was only identified in 1992[249]). Scientists have now made a smaller effective form of the gene. There is some evidence that temporary improvement may be possible following its injection into the muscles of mice with a similar disease.

The technique was discovered by accident: in an experiment involving mice, genes contained in artificial cell membranes were being injected into muscle to see what would happen. As a control, a second group of mice had genetic code injected directly into muscle. Research workers were surprised to find that the control group did best. In five out of a hundred cases, reprogramming resulted. Further experiments have increased this percentage. Such genes appear to go on working in muscle for several months at least. This technique only seems to work in muscle.[250] An alternative might be to infect muscle cells using adapted and reprogrammed herpes or hepatitis viruses.[251]

Now scientists have taken a big step further forward in the fight against DMD. A similar genetic defect in mice has been corrected successfully by inserting a new gene into viruses and using the viruses to infect mice embryos. However, the technique only worked with one mouse out of the group and even then the inserted gene only worked at one-sixth of the normal level.[252]

Preventing brain and blood disorders

There are many other diseases where such an approach is being considered. For example, some children are born with a problem with their metabolism called phenylketonuria (PKU). This can cause brain damage if not picked up at birth. The best treatment of all would be to program back the defective gene in liver cells after birth.[253]

Another genetic disorder attracting attention is a disorder of red blood cell haemoglobin called thalassaemia. Many attempts are being made with mammal cells to reprogram cells back, so offering a hope of cure. So far progress here is disappointingly slow.[254] With all of these blood disorders you only have to reprogram a few bone marrow cells to produce a result since these cells have a vast potential to reproduce themselves. Recent progress in mice gave 100% success with every mouse reconstituted with at least one reprogrammed cell.[255]

Psychiatrists have been warned to prepare themselves for further counselling of people with the inherited type of Alzheimer's disease (pre-senile dementia).[256] The defective gene responsible for some cases of Alzheimer's disease was discovered in 1991. As a result, some people have already been offered genetic screening—an agonising option a few have refused. Information can create tension and problems, for example arising out of a decision not to have children, rather than freedom of choice and liberty.[257] Ethical issues are likely to become more complex as our understanding and range of interventions grow. Many other brain or psychiatric illnesses may also have a genetic component.[258]

Reprogramming sperm and eggs

Another approach might be to reprogram faulty human sperm or eggs.[259] This is likely to be difficult. Only quite a low percentage of embryos developing would be successfully reprogrammed and there would be enormous difficulty in detecting which were, if the aim of those involved was to abort 'non-successes'.

However, the most effective way of all would be to reprogram human cells directly using viruses. We can do this routinely in monkeys.[260] Such gene therapy could be used for disorders of bone marrow, liver, central nervous system, some kinds of cancer, deficiencies of circulating enzymes, hormones and coagulation factors. By using viruses which normally cause disease, we are 'turning the swords of pathology into the ploughshares of therapy'.[261] However, we have to be absolutely sure that such viruses, when given as medicines, infect cells, reprogram them and are then destroyed. Otherwise a risk exists that the treatment could be infectious: treat one child and the whole school takes the medicine.[262]

Gene spray for cystic fibrosis

An aerosol spray of live viruses could well become a normal everyday treatment for those with cystic fibrosis, the most common inherited disease affecting one in 2,500 babies. Cystic fibrosis affects around 6,000 people in the UK and is caused by a lack of genetic code in mucus-secreting cells to produce a particular substance to keep secretions runny. As a result, those with the condition produce abnormal amounts of thick mucus— especially a problem in the lungs where small airways tend to become blocked and chest infections become a major problem.

The defective gene was identified in 1989. Few used to survive beyond their twentieth birthday, but better treatments mean a large number are now surviving longer—until middle age. Research has shown that new genetic code can be programmed into cells in the lungs of animals by aerosols.[263] Researchers in the USA have managed to introduce a functioning cystic fibrosis gene into the lungs of cotton rats. They placed copies of the gene into another type of virus (adenovirus) especially modified so that it could still infect the lungs, but not reproduce. The gene was active for six weeks.[264]

The treatment could be given either by a simple hand-held puffer like those used for asthma, or by a nebuliser used with a face mask (a nebuliser turns a liquid into a very fine mist which can be breathed in). An alternative might be to remove and modify white cells (T lymphocytes), transplanting them back into the lungs after reprogramming. This has been success-fully tried in mice, although the results were short-lived.[265]

Gene therapy 'within five years'

Specialists believe such a 'gene therapy' could well be available within five to ten years. However, there are safety hurdles to be overcome first. The adenovirus could regain the ability to reproduce by recombining with naturally occurring adeno-viruses in the lungs. If this happened, then tens of thousands in a town or city could be accidentally infected following treat-ment of just one person with cystic fibrosis—with unpredictable and potentially disastrous results.[266]

St Mary's Hospital in London recently received £1,000,000

from the Cystic Fibrosis Trust to help find a gene treatment.[267] Attempts are being made to make special artificial chromosomes— 'minichromosomes'—containing replacement genes and the machinery for them to duplicate when cells divide.[268]

Real progress still slow

Such genetic 'cures' could revolutionise lives, even if they have to be used daily for life. However, such gene therapies are hardly likely to make a massive contribution to fighting human illnesses since, as we have seen, only two in a hundred are ill simply as a result of a gene problem.[269] It is true that many illnesses such as heart disease may have a genetic component, but the only ones likely to be suitable for gene therapy at the present time are those caused by 'single gene defects'.

Even for single gene defects, real progress towards cure is still agonisingly slow, both for those ill and those who care for them. Some doctors involved believe the technological limits are still far bigger hurdles to overcome than 'the ethical boundaries proposed by moral philosophers and newspaper columnists'.[270]

Using genes to fight cancer

We have already seen how monoclonal antibodies have been helpful in fighting cancer or in developing new experimental treatments. However, a more direct approach would be to try to reverse any genetic damage if that is the reason for the cells dividing out of control in the first place.

Cancer cells are basically like any others in the body from which they developed. The only real difference is that cancer cells, by definition, do not know when to stop growing and dividing, so large balls of cells develop instead of normal tissue. These rapidly-growing cells can cause chaos by using up a lot of food and energy, and by blocking normal function of body organs. Some of these cells also release things into the blood— but usually just overproducing normal substances.

Scientists have been experimenting with skin cells from patients prone to a particular, rare kind of cancer called the Basal Cell Nevus Syndrome.[271] They have found that these cells (fibroblasts) differ genetically from normal and are liable to start dividing uncontrollably if exposed to particular chemicals or naturally occurring body substances. Rectifying such genetic differences could be a part of cancer cures in the future.[272]

Gene fixes for bowel cancer

One of the first examples of cancer which might be cured by genetic reprogramming of tumour cells could turn out to be the inherited forms of colon cancer. In these cells, a particular cancer-suppressing gene called 'p53' appears to be missing, so these cells tend to grow uncontrollably. The same abnormal p53 gene seems to be present in 70% of lung cancers which kill 40,000 people a year in the UK alone.[273]

The John Hopkins Oncology Centre in Baltimore USA has succeeded in transforming colon cancer cells back to normal by inserting the correct p53 gene into cancer cells grown in the laboratory.[274] As we have seen, the gene acts as a natural brake on cells, causing them to function normally and divide only when necessary to repair or replace bowel lining. The reprogrammed cells then divide at only a tenth of their previous rate.

However, there are many practical problems to overcome before this could become a viable treatment in humans. For a start we would need to make a specific virus for colon cells and be sure it was completely safe. This is probably around ten years away still. In the meantime, we may be able to produce drugs based on the protein that the p53 gene makes. The protein may turn out to control the tumour well.

Conventional treatment kills healthy cells

For the last thirty years the main anti-cancer weapon we have used has been very clumsy. We have developed chemicals that damage cells as they try to divide. In an earlier chapter we saw how they prevent the genetic code from being duplicated into two, so the cell is stuck in the middle of division. Radiotherapy treatment using radioactivity also works in the same way by damaging the genetic material—something most likely to happen in cells as they start to divide.

You might think this is an ideal approach to cancer—after

all, non-dividing normal cells such as brain and kidney cells should be unaffected. Unfortunately, many cells in the body do divide as rapidly as cancer cells and these too can tend to be severely damaged. Obvious examples are hair-producing cells, skin cells, bone marrow cells (producing red and white blood cells) and the cells lining the gut.

Sometimes we can find types of cancer which need human hormones to carry on growing. This is especially true of some cancers that have grown from the reproductive organs. In these cases we can see excellent results in some by giving medicines to block normal hormone production. However, for the vast majority of cancers we are still unable to destroy them selectively without damage elsewhere.

Human messengers of death

One answer being investigated is to program human cells so they themselves produce the chemotherapy agent being used to fight the cancer cells. Injecting a solution of these factory cells directly into the tumour should then cause the cancer cells to receive a very high dose, while tiny amounts of agent leaking out into the rest of the body should be so dilute as to prevent any damage elsewhere. Initial good results have already been seen in mice with transplanted human tumours injected with reprogrammed factory cells. The cells used were fibroblasts reprogrammed by infection with specially prepared retroviruses.[275]

Genes to stop growing old

For centuries people have tried to make an elixir of everlasting youth: a substance to arrest the natural process of growing old. Indeed some people will go to amazing lengths to help ensure their physical immortality, even arranging for their heads to be cut off moments after death and frozen in liquid nitrogen until medical advances make a 'resurrection' possible. Such a process of 'cryonic suspension' costs around £30,000 and is available from a centre in Eastbourne, England, in partnership with a headquarters in California.

When death comes, a non-clotting agent is injected into the veins and other drugs added to stabilise the metabolism of the body. All the blood is then drained away and replaced with an anti-freeze mixture. The head is then amputated, cooled rapidly, and placed in a steel container for transport to California. The rest of the body is incinerated. Whole body suspension is available, but is double the price.[276] The fact that some people will go to such lengths to fight death demonstrates why there is so much interest in arresting the ageing process.

Ageing is still a mystery to doctors and research scientists because many cells do not age at all and go on healthily dividing for ever. Examples are stem cells in the bone marrow and cancer cells—the same cells used to make monoclonal antibodies in the laboratory.

Theories of ageing include a genetic time clock, progressive genetic damage occurring with time through many cell generations, or the accumulation of certain substances inside the cell which interfere with normal function.[277] Evidence is growing to support the latter, with the discovery of 'ageing pigments' in muscle and nerve cells. Could gene changes help overcome this? In theory there is no logical reason why we should not be able to design new cells with specialist functions but able to go on dividing faithfully for ever—or to stop dividing when told to do so by the body.

Human bodies to live for ever?

A leading British expert on ageing said recently that it seems people grow old because our genes treat our bodies as disposable goods. It could therefore be theoretically possible for humans to live for ever provided their genes are programmed to correct for the wear-and-tear of life. Scientists are involved in a three-year research programme to discover some of the secrets of eternal youth, believing that the average human lifespan can be extended. By studying cells from creatures like mice which die after a maximum of three years, and comparing with human cells, we will be able to see more clearly how ageing is controlled.[278]

Having looked at a great number of new medical advances, we now turn to one of the strangest and most powerful of all: using germ warfare against other germs—a virus to catch a virus.

7

A Virus to Catch a Virus

We now come to one of the most extraordinary advances ever made by genetic engineers: germ warfare directed against germs. The idea of using one organism to fight another is not new. Some years ago the virus causing myxomatosis in rabbits was deliberately introduced into Australia in an attempt to control the numbers of wild rabbits, which were ruining crops. The disease spread much more rapidly than intended, wiping out millions of rabbits so that the population was still low years later.

AIDS—laboratory accident or natural disaster?

The new human disease that dominates so many headlines in the 1990s is AIDS, which stands for Acquired Immune Deficiency Syndrome. It is caused by a virus that some have speculated at times was made in a germ laboratory and released as a result of an accident. We now know that the virus called HIV has been around much longer than the facilities to make it in the laboratory—certainly since before 1959.[279] People went on to suggest that the virus had been forced to alter in the laboratory from an animal strain by using samples to infect a wide variety of animals under strange conditions.

When such infections are forced on creatures usually immune to a virus, the result can often be a change in the virus structure, particularly if it recombines with another naturally occurring virus in the animal. Such mutations can make the virus more infectious and able to infect different species. It is theoretically possible (but very unlikely) that such experiments could have accelerated the development of HIV from animal viruses of a very similar nature.

What is certain however is that we now have the tools to take viruses apart and put them back together again. No longer do we need to rely on the random effects of the animal host. These changes can now be programmed in the test-tube with far greater confidence.

AIDS epidemic out of control

Many of the attempts to find an AIDS cure or a vaccine depend on genetic engineering. The drive to find a cure is intense because the problem is so massive. Already the lives of 13 million people hang on finding a cure—around one in 250 of all adults alive today. The virus can live in the body for fifteen years or more before causing disease, so for some there is still time. Meanwhile, the infection spreads. Almost every country of the world is now reporting cases.

While the European situation has turned out to be slightly less severe than feared, the two-thirds world has been severely hit. In many African towns and cities, up to one in three of all the sexually active adults are infected.

Despite public perceptions, HIV is predominantly an infection spread through heterosexual sex, accounting for seven out of ten infections worldwide so far, and nine out of ten infections in 1992.[280] It is true however that most infection in the UK has been among gay men, and much of the remainder among drug users. The World Health Organisation estimated in 1992 that by the turn of the century there would already be some 10 million children orphaned as a result of AIDS, with a further 10 million children infected from birth.[281]

Search for AIDS vaccine

Normal vaccines don't work

Gene research has concentrated mainly on developing a vaccine against HIV. One way of vaccinating people is to take normal virus particles and damage them so they are incapable of causing infection. If they are injected into people, their white cells will see the damaged particles as foreign and destroy them. As a result, their immune systems will be prepared for the real thing in the future with no risk of disease.

Such vaccines do not work with HIV for several reasons. The first is that damaged viruses do not bother the immune system very much and the body tends to ignore them. Because of this the value of the learning experience for the body is much less. The second reason is that the virus is very variable. While the flu virus undergoes a change in shape every few months or years somewhere in the world, HIV is so unstable that even in the same person you will find hundreds of different-shaped variations, each of which may require a slightly different-shaped antibody to fight it. Experience has shown that HIV is effectively immune from all known human antibodies. After all, almost everyone infected produces antibodies without being able to get rid of the virus.

Making bits of HIV

An alternative to injecting damaged HIV particles is to manufacture defective HIV which can also be injected without the risk of infection. Most of the experimental vaccines have been made by inserting genes from HIV into bacteria or other cells. As a result, they produce non-infectious fragments of HIV outer coating which can be injected into humans. The body reacts by producing antibodies against these fragments.

Scientists now think they have found a few parts of the virus structure which change much less often, and these are the parts being manufactured.[282] A company called MicroGenesys makes parts called gp160 in insect cells, while Immuno makes gp160 in cells of mammals. Oncogen makes gp160 as part of vaccinia virus while Chiron/Ciba Geigy makes gp120 in yeast cells.

Genentech and British Biotechnology are also making fragments containing p24, yet another viral building block. Trials on limited numbers of healthy volunteers and HIV carriers are now under way using gp24, while US Congress has just approved $20 million for a large-scale trial of gp160.[283] All these vaccines are highly experimental, but are much safer than injecting whole HIV particles—however certain we may be that they have been completely deactivated.[284]

Milder strains of HIV

You can try to get a better response to a vaccine by creating a new virus which is capable of causing infection but not disease. Sometimes you find these milder strains occurring naturally. The cowpox virus produces very mild illness compared to smallpox, but because both viruses have identical outer coatings, infection with cowpox in the past produces protection against smallpox in the future. Attempts have been made to do this with HIV.

Billions of dollars every year are being poured into this process—trying to find a way to produce antibodies in people that will protect against HIV. Almost every week research papers are published reporting steady progress. However, even if a vaccine is found which appears to produce antibodies in humans protecting against HIV, it will be many years before we will have long enough experience of its use to be sure it is safe and truly effective. Even when a good vaccine comes it is unlikely to eradicate the virus from the millions who are already infected, although stimulation of the immune system may help in treatment.

In the meantime, disturbing reports are emerging that antibodies which protect early on in HIV infection may accelerate development of illness later on. A vaccine against one strain may make someone more likely to die quickly from another.[285]

We also need to find a vaccine that will work against a second major type of HIV, called HIV-2. This is gradually spreading from countries in West Africa where it was first identified in the mid-1980s. Almost certainly the development of this vaccine too will be a direct result of genetic engineering.[286]

Search for AIDS cure

Genetic engineers are also trying to find an AIDS cure. These treatments are all very experimental and can be hazardous. For example, inserting genetic code from HIV into a live vaccinia virus (cowpox) resulted in severe vaccinia disease in two people with AIDS when they were injected with the newly engineered virus. It had been hoped that the new virus would stimulate the immune system vigorously to produce a reaction to HIV. Instead it appears that undamaged vaccinia virus produced severe vaccinia disease in patients with AIDS whose immune systems were too weak to fight it.

How HIV works

To find a safe and effective cure we first have to identify how HIV operates inside the cell and decide which part of the machine to jam. Viruses contain a small section of genetic writing—usually just enough instructions to tell the infected cell to stop all normal factory production and instead to produce millions more viruses. The virus does this by several methods. As we have seen, the virus causing AIDS does it by reversing the normal chain of command in the cell.

Usually genes inside the nucleus direct the cell, giving out messages to tell the cell factories what to do. In this case, a form of genetic code (RNA) injected into the cell is used as a messenger in reverse, using an enzyme called reverse transcriptase to alter genes inside the nucleus. The main anti-AIDS drug used (Zidovudine) is a drug which is used to try and block the activity of this enzyme. Once the book of life inside the nucleus has been permanently altered, every cell formed as a result of growth and division will be similarly affected.

Using a computer analogy, the virus is a computer disk and the nucleus is the memory of the computer. The computer disk is corrupt and fills the computer with incorrect programs. It seems obvious that the answer to treating such cells is to program them back to normal using a second virus as you would a new manufacturer's computer disk.

Internal antibodies

If human white cells in the test-tube are exposed to reverse transcriptase, or to some other piece of machinery, one in 10,000 will start to produce specific antibodies to it. The production of the specific antibody by reacting cells will be controlled by the genes of the cell using specific instructions carried from the nucleus as messenger RNA (see p 37). If we can extract this special RNA, we can use it to make DNA with the same coding. This can then be used to alter genes of bone marrow cells removed from people carrying HIV.

These reprogrammed bone marrow cells should then start to produce antibodies against reverse transcriptase. They should now have some protection against the virus because virus particles entering the cell will find antibodies inside the cell are destroying the enzyme needed to reprogram the nucleus. At the moment such an approach is theoretical only. Cells could also be programmed to produce other anti-viral substances within the cells themselves. This 'star wars' approach to anti-viral therapy is being developed by a research team in Boston, USA, but is still at an early stage.[287]

We could also program cells to make antibodies against HIV which are active inside cells instead of being released into the blood. This approach is known as 'pathogen-derived resistance'. Such genes could be made and tested quite easily on white cells in the laboratory, before attempting to use them as 'gene therapy' in people already HIV-infected.[288]

Anti-virus to repair altered cells

In 1987 I wrote a book called *The Truth About AIDS*, which contained up-to-date information on the epidemic gleaned from hundreds of recently published scientific papers.[289] I speculated then that scientists might by the turn of the century be able to make an anti-virus: a new virus to reverse the effects of the previous one. If HIV works by altering genes in the cell, how about using a second virus to program the cell back to normal? How realistic is this?

As we have seen in earlier chapters, altering animal cells to produce human substances is becoming quite routine. For example, in 1987 animal cells were grown in a test-tube and successfully reprogrammed using special techniques[290] so that when implanted into mice they produced human growth hormone. The implanted cells tended to be destroyed by the mice and none was still active after three months. However, the experiment was a real breakthrough.[291]

Changing the genes of animal cells is also a relatively predictable technique because reprogrammed cells can be observed carefully to see how they behave before implantation. So what about using viruses to reverse damage done to cells of mammals? Retroviruses have been used already to reprogram liver cells successfully[292] and bone marrow cells in monkeys.[293]

Designing new viruses

Building viruses is surprisingly straightforward, given their complexity once assembled. Most viruses are built from basic structures like identical pieces of Lego, moulded so they can only be assembled one way. These pieces attract each other and fit together so well that if millions of them are placed in a liquid, they tend to join up spontaneously, in exactly the right shape, built around a core of genetic code. We can even build virus outer shells with no genes inside. We can also program cells to make them. Such experiments have been carried out using human cells to make empty shells of a virus which causes bone marrow failure in children.[294]

Virus repairs for sickle cell disease

Sickle cell disease is a disease affecting red blood cell haemoglobin. Genetically caused, it is extremely common in Africa and the Middle East because these unusually shaped red cells provide some resistance to malaria, so people with sickle cell genes tend to survive longer and have more children. Unfortunately, when oxygen levels in the body fall for any reason, these abnormal red cells alter shape (into a sickle shape seen under the microscope) and clump together, blocking blood vessels and causing serious problems. Researchers are trying to infect bone marrow cells with viruses to program back the faulty genes.[295]

How to undo viral damage

The way to undo viral damage could be to:

1.   Construct viruses containing both the normal human gene for haemoglobin (beta-globin gene) and a suitable marker gene so we can tell if the cells have been successfully altered (see p 71).

2.   Remove some bone marrow cells from someone with sickle cell disease.

3.   Destroy all remaining bone marrow cells by radiotherapy.

4.   Infect the removed cells in the laboratory, selecting out those reprogrammed by using the marker.

5.   Transplant back the person's own reprogrammed cells.

A virus to catch a virus

To reprogram HIV-infected white cells we can take a similar approach. First we need to make a new virus with an identical outside coating so it sticks onto and affects the identical cells in the body, but with the correct genetic message inside. Huge progress has been made: in 1987 scientists took human bone marrow cells and successfully infected them with a virus containing genetic code with a marker for resistance to an antibiotic called neomycin.

They did it by mixing bone marrow cells in a liquid containing a high concentration of viruses from virus-producing cells. They managed to reprogram up to 16% of the bone marrow cells by this method.[296] The virus type used was very similar in action to the virus causing AIDS, also called a retrovirus because it also uses RNA from the virus to change the DNA in genes of the cell.

Gene cure for immune deficiency

A major step towards gene cure of immune deficiency was recently announced following controversial research on children.[297] The disease was not AIDS, but a very similar deficiency of the immune system present at birth as an inherited illness rather than one happening as a result of virus infection. The disease is called ADA for short.[298] Children born with

ADA as a result of a gene mutation should not be confused with those born who will later develop AIDS as a result of being HIV-infected from the mother via the womb.

Bone marrow cells (T-type white cells) were taken from a four-year-old girl with the illness and infected with viruses containing a normal copy of the ADA gene. The reprogrammed cells were then grown in the laboratory and then transfused back into the person again. Cells transfused back were correctly producing the missing substance for up to forty days after reintroduction. The experiment was carried out in September 1990 by the US National Institute of Health. The effects are not permanent because the cells only have a short lifespan. Similar work is also being carried out in the UK.[299]

Now attempts are being made to program stem cells in the bone marrow which are immortal—they go on dividing for ever and are the parents of all the specialised cells produced in the bone marrow. The cells are hard to find, accounting for less than one in 10,000 bone marrow cells, but can now be selected by using monoclonal antibodies, made as we have seen through genetic engineering.[300] Such therapies could be available quite soon on an experimental basis to those with HIV. However, one further technical problem will need to be overcome.

Locking viruses out of cells

Viruses are very sophisticated structures. There is a second message in almost all viruses which is designed to stop another virus from being able to enter the same cell. Viruses like to have sole occupation it seems. It can get very confusing if two types of virus are being built inside cells at the same time. We have already seen how they can recombine to form hybrids or mutations with unpredictable results (see page 113).

The chemical made by human cells as a response to viral infection is called interferon. Unless we can find a way of neutralising its effects, we could find it almost impossible to get a second virus into a cell already infected. Another approach has been to use bacteria to produce huge amounts of interferon to be given as a medicine. The hope would be to protect all the cells in the body from viral attack. This has been tried for cancers and for AIDS with results which have been very disappointing on the whole. Interferon injections also cause flu-like symptoms and the drug is very expensive.

HIV cure may lead to cure for colds

Once we begin to build anti-viruses accurately and with confidence, we will find almost overnight a revolution has taken place in medicine. Not only will we have the ultimate cure for HIV infection, but also for flu and a host of other viral infections, including sore throats and pneumonia. We may well find in the future that diseases like multiple sclerosis also have a viral origin and can be similarly cured.

Much attention is being focused on the common cold, produced by around 120 different types of virus called rhinoviruses.[301] These viruses are highly variable, so you can catch the same strain of cold virus several times in a lifetime—by the time it hits you a second or third time, its outer coating is so altered as to be unrecognisable by the body's immune system.

All cold viruses have one thing in common: they all have a surface feature which can latch onto cells lining the inside of the nose. These nose cells are unique in the body, which is why cold viruses do not give you spots on your skin or, say, cause diarrhoea. Over 80% of the viruses attach to exactly the same component of the walls of cells in the nose. This whole component (surface receptor molecule) has been genetically engineered.[302] Perhaps one day we will have a nasal spray of surface receptor molecules made by genetic engineering which—if used twice a day—will mean cold viruses entering the nose latch onto false receptors and are immobilised.

False white cell walls to trick HIV

A similar approach is already being tried in humans with HIV: here the receptors on T4 white cells are called CD4 and are the ones the virus causing AIDS is shaped to lock onto. Genetically engineered CD4 has been produced in vast quantities in the laboratory and injected as an experimental treatment. Results so far have been poor, partly because the body destroys these particles very fast, and they have to be injected regularly to keep the blood concentration high. Such a treatment would need to be taken for life.

How long for a cure or vaccine?

The massive global research programme to find a vaccine or cure for AIDS will have the same effect on speeding up the gene revolution as the US space programme in the 1960s and 1970s had on the development of microchips and portable computers. Quite when we will have a vaccine or cure for HIV and AIDS is still uncertain. Because of time delays between vaccine development and completion of testing, a widely available effective vaccine is highly unlikely before the year 2000. By the turn of the century we should have seen some major advances towards developing effective treatments, although again safety testing and high cost are likely to delay widespread use considerably, and a permanent cure is likely to be much further away.

Permanent hair colourant

The result of such advances could mean that many medicines or treatments in the future will only need to be given once in a lifetime. Synthetic viruses open up many curious possibilities. In 1987 I first raised the possibility of permanent hair colourant. We are a hundred steps nearer. If you want blonde hair instead of brown, then one day you may be able to go into a chemist's and buy a bottle of hair follicle virus.

The viruses in the hair colourant bottle would have an outside coating that fits only to cells which make hair. They would contain the instructions for fair hair instead of dark. If by some accident a few other different cells in the body were also infected, the results would be unnoticeable. After all, stomach cells do not use that part of the book of life anyway, so however much it is altered the stomach cells would continue as normal. Unless the virus medicine also infects the cells producing eggs or sperm, then such changes would die with the person and would not be passed on to the next generation.

Redesigning your own body

The implications of all this are mind-stretching. Perhaps an adult could buy a change of skin colour. We should be able to turn on or off all kinds of instructions that certain cells use every day. We should certainly be able to cure a great many cancers. A tumour sample would be analysed and the code checked for the fault. This would then be corrected with a virus injection. For many cancers we may find that there are a number of faults which are very common, so one medicine may cure several different cancers rather than different viruses needing to be designed for each one.

Medicines to cure your grandchildren

The outlook should improve dramatically for those who discover that they have an inherited disease. In addition to obvious major diseases such as haemophilia, we should also be able to deal with faulty genes that occur in most of the population. As we have already seen, some genes are more likely to produce strokes, while others are more likely to produce breast cancer, eczema, asthma, or a tendency to certain mental problems. None of these things is certain unless you have a single gene disease like haemophilia.

There is therefore a huge market for genetic cleaning techniques: viruses to infect eggs or sperm to make sure that your own children are less likely than your parents were to drop down dead of heart attacks before they are sixty years old, for example. Such techniques will need to be refined extensively in animals before trying on humans.

For someone with major genetic disease in themselves or their family, gene modification or selection of embryos on the basis of genes may be the only chance the person is willing to take to have a child. However, the greatest problem of all is being sure modification has taken place, and has happened safely without accidentally introducing other mutations. By removing a cell from an embryo before implanting in the womb, or from a foetus within the womb, it might be possible to check on the genetic makeup. It is much more difficult to make a full analysis of the eggs or sperm to check the code is now satisfactory before allowing conception to occur.

Now we have seen how gene changes can transform farming and medicine by altering the basic design of life itself, we have to ask the most important questions of all: could the gene revolution destroy us, or the world in which we live? What is the future of life on earth?

8

Could New Genes Destroy Us?

Having looked at the enormous benefits to agriculture and medicine as a result of genetic engineering, we now need to look at the possible dangers before then thinking about changes in the law or other regulations.

There are good reasons to be concerned about the risks:[303] 'We have to be aware of the high risks and responsibility of everybody who is involved in these new systems, especially the scientist who produces genetically engineered organisms.'[304] On a purely practical level, we need to look in detail at some of the things that could go wrong. Virulent new infections threatening to wipe us all out is the substance of science fiction films such as *Star Trek*, but what is the reality?

1. New organisms going out of control

The idea that an organism could do great damage if released in the wrong place is not new; it is based on bitter experience. Those concerned for the environment can point to a large number of times where plants or animals introduced from one country into another have unexpectedly become a nuisance. Therefore there has been enormous concern over what could happen if a genetically altered species were released into the environment with unexpected results.[305]

A plague of rhododendrons

We have already seen the unpredictable dangers of releasing viruses with the myxomatosis epidemic among rabbits in Australia. Another example of unexpected problems is the current plague of rhododendrons in Snowdonia and other parts of the UK. This plant was imported from India for the first time in the eighteenth century by wealthy landowners who liked the evergreen bushes with their dark fleshy leaves that grow well in woodland and have magnificent flowers. The bushes grow very densely, cutting out all light beneath. They grow tall and then flop over, suffocating nearby plants or young growing trees. They also disturb the balance of the soil, turning it more acidic. You might think this would not matter too much—we all appreciate country walks through wild woodlands rich with the beauty of these flowers.

The problem is that the plants are just too resilient. Some 250 different types of insects, fungi, or small creatures live off a single oak tree. This ecological system maintains a rich balanced environment and keeps oak trees from totally dominating the countryside. Compared to the oak, the rhododendron is a very unfriendly plant. The leaves are juicy but unpleasant to eat, so even in a deer park they may be left alone. The leaves have virtually no food value, even if they are eaten. There are very few creatures that thrive on rhododendron bushes—no fruits to eat or nuts to collect or useful sap to drink.

The bushes are spreading steadily, escaping from where they were planted originally. When cut down they just grow up again. In places like Snowdonia they have become a ferocious weed which conservationists are despairing at, yet no one could possibly have predicted this when they were planted there over 100 years ago. So then, it is sometimes hazardous enough to move even a naturally occurring organism from one country or area to another, but what about introducing an organism the world has never met before—anywhere?[306]

Super-weeds, super-breeds and super-bugs

What will be the effects of hundreds of new plants created in the laboratory and released into the environment? How can we be sure that a particular cereal plant will not turn into a nuisance? Transgenic fish could also cause vast problems: as we have seen, a number of new fish types or variants of species have already been created. What will happen if they are released into rivers or the sea where they become more successful than anticipated in competing for the food chain, leading to extinction of many other species?[307] The answer is that no one knows without releasing organisms to find out—and the results could be different for each different mutation.

New super-weeds could also develop, with resistance to weed-killers, if cross-fertilisation were to occur between common weeds and new gene modified cereals resistant to herbicides.

The area that possibly gives most cause for concern is the invisible one of new strains of bacteria or viruses finding their way out of the gene factory and into the soil, water supply or the bodies of animals or humans with potentially disastrous results.[308] Such new strains are now becoming available commercially and, as they do, control is becoming more difficult with every day that passes.[309]

Bacteria spread uncontrollably between humans

We have seen earlier that genetic engineers often use bacteria which grow naturally in the human gut and which can be found elsewhere. What would be the effect of creating by accident a new version of E.coli which turned out to release substances causing bowel cancer if they got into the human gut? This strain might have been designed originally to have some other useful genetically engineered feature, such as the ability to produce hormones to increase cow milk production.

E.coli organisms pass all the time between humans despite normal standards of cleanliness—just as well that they do or newborn babies would suffer through lack of them and people on antibiotics would have permanent bowel problems afterwards if E.coli were killed. It is impossible therefore to control the spread of a strain of E.coli through a town or city. We see this in the spread of resistance to antibiotics. If you treat a certain percentage of a town with certain antibiotics, before long you can find there are resistant E.coli in the guts of those who have never been treated with antibiotics in their lives. Fortunately, resistance is usually lost with time, unlike a genetically engineered organism which could remain dangerous for a very long period, be hard to detect and impossible to control.

Threat of soil contamination

What about water supplies or soil? Soil organisms are also used in genetic engineering and tampering with the genetic code of a non-soil organism could produce one which was able to survive in the soil quite well, or could turn a harmless soil organism into a global hazard.[310] Are we producing domesticated bacteria or potential 'andromeda strains'?[311] Suppose such an organism turned out to survive very well indeed, and to multiply fast—or suppose it travelled further in an agricultural spray than it was meant to. We know very little about how genetically engineered bacteria might be carried in a strong wind from, say, a small crop-spraying aeroplane or helicopter.

Microcomputer programs are being developed to try to predict what could happen, but there are an enormous number of variables, including particle size, wind speed and direction, turbulence, evaporation, sedimentation and bacterial survival time.[312] Survival time and what the organisms release into the soil are the two critical factors. Suppose we make a mistake, and one organism in 100,000 in the spray mix turns out to be an undetected mutant, but with quite unexpected and terrible results.

Predicting danger

Studies are being carried out to see how well bacteria survive in agricultural sprays. In one study in a greenhouse, bean and oat plants were sprayed with bacteria in an attempt to simulate what might happen in a field. Damp air (high humidity) and low temperature made bacterial growth on the plants up to sixty-five times more likely after spraying. Bacteria also survive better if the spray contains larger droplets rather than small.[313] Drifting downwind was noted, but the strain being used tended not to establish itself unless concentrations on the plants were high.[314]

Studies are also continuing to see how well genetically engineered bacteria survive in soil.[315] Do they get washed through by rainwater? Will they end up in streams and rivers or pollute our reservoirs? Such studies are difficult and time consuming. They have to be done in artificial conditions—after all, the whole point is to check first before releasing into the environment. How well will such studies match up to conditions in the outside world?

You cannot sterilise the entire planet

The pressure is growing therefore to allow small-scale introduction of genetically engineered micro-organisms into the soil. The company Monsanto has developed a new strain of bacteria which is fluorescent, to monitor the passage of the bacteria through soil more easily. This strain has been used first in a pre-release growth chamber and then in a limited field test. The tests were approved by the US Environmental Protection Agency.[316]

Suppose that such bacteria release acids or other chemicals into the soil that make the soil unusable.[317] Suppose that such organisms are carried in dust on car wheels, on shoes, by strong winds, on the feet of animals or by insects. The effects could be devastating on an area, a country, or a continent. This is perhaps one of the most worrying scenarios since it would be totally impossible to put right. After all, you cannot sterilise the entire planet.

Altered bacteria survive in lakes and fields

Further studies have looked at the survival of genetically changed bacteria in lakes. The experiments were carried out in special flow chambers where the water was constantly changing to simulate as closely as possible natural conditions after release. Scientists have found that strains of altered bacteria tested tend to survive as well as the originals.[318] Similar results with E.coli bacteria in drinking water show that both original and altered types tested die off quickly.[319] Clearly survival can be greatly improved or lessened, depending on how the organisms are modified.

Other experiments have looked at how easy it is to destroy genetically engineered bacteria once their function is completed or if adverse environmental effects are discovered. Field plots of bush beans were sprayed with bacteria and then either tilled using farming equipment, or burned, or sprayed with herbicide. Herbicides were useless, while tilling actually increased the number of bacteria surviving. Only burning was found to reduce the numbers of bacteria significantly more than doing nothing at all.[320]

Even where there are strict regulations, unauthorised release of new organisms is already happening.[321] Sometimes this has been carried out by those who believe the risks to be minimal,[322] and just a natural extension of evolutionary principles and an expansion of the process of domestication of species.[323]

Dangers from escaped viruses

New viruses could also cause major disasters. As we have seen, there have already been suggestions that the AIDS epidemic caused by HIV could have started as a result of a laboratory accident (see p 122). Although we have dismissed this theory as being very unlikely, we are faced with the fact that in the 1990s we now have the ability to create tens of thousands of new viruses, many of which may have unpredictable results. Some of them will be relatively harmless and may be suitable as vaccines,[324] while others may turn out to be more lethal or more infectious. In the case of infectious HIV variants, the only way to find out is on humans, because HIV cannot function properly in animals.

Viruses can and do escape. Why else did the World Health Organisation insist that the last surviving specimens of smallpox were destroyed? The nightmare became a reality in 1982 in Birmingham University when a sample escaped from a damaged container and a laboratory worker became infected. She died, and a major outbreak of smallpox was only prevented because the people she had come into contact with had been vaccinated in the past.

Smallpox escaped again

More worryingly, this was not the first such accident: in 1973 a smallpox outbreak at the London School of Hygiene and Tropical Medicine killed two people.[325] Smallpox infection has now been completely eradicated worldwide by a global vaccination programme. Because of this, smallpox vaccination programmes have now stopped. If a similar accident were to happen in ten or twenty years' time, a vast epidemic could result, because tens of millions of people born after vaccination ceased would have no protection.

Fortunately (if we believe the laboratories concerned), all last remaining viruses have been destroyed. Perhaps they have not been. The temptation is very great to keep such a powerful virus from extinction for those who might want to tamper with it genetically now or in the future. Scientists can also be as untidy and disorganised as the rest of the population.

In 1985 the London School of Hygiene and Tropical Medicine was involved in yet another smallpox scare when sealed ampoules of virus were found by accident in a fridge in the medical microbiology department—inside a biscuit tin where they had been since 1952.[326] If such mistakes can happen with smallpox—known to be one of the most infectious and dangerous viruses ever discovered—then it is obvious that accidents are going to happen quite routinely with viruses thought to be relatively harmless.[327]

Industrial accidents growing more likely

There is also the possibility of industrial accidents as the number of factories growing genetically engineered organisms continues to increase. For each kind of bacteria, filamentous fungus, yeast, mammalian cell and virus, the risks can be quite separate and different. For example, the main risk to factory or laboratory workers from bacteria is infections of various kinds. Vast culture banks exist in this country, containing samples of thousands of cell cultures and organisms, some held to record a patent.[328]

For cell cultures, the main risk is considered to be from undetected dormant viruses inside the cells, which later become activated and dangerous. Although good management of cultures should eliminate these, when you are talking about work in hundreds of laboratories across the globe it has to be recognised that standards cannot be guaranteed. A recent report evaluating the range of risks came to the conclusion that they were small—but also had to admit that such conclusions remained theoretical, in the absence of any reported occupational accidents or diseases attributed directly to genetically engineered organisms. The study concluded that 'only long-term observations can confirm this assumption [low risk] and consequently the highest feasible containment measures should still be used in years to come'.[329]

Cancer risk from some gene medicines

A further worry has been accidental infection of patients with viruses causing cancer as a result of injection with substances obtained from altered human cells. These cells are usually cancerous in origin (or else they tend not to go on dividing in the laboratory) and cancers are sometimes triggered by viruses. Viral material could contaminate these new medicines and be injected accidentally with increased risk of cancer in the future. This is very unlikely to happen if proper procedures are followed, but the possibility continues to cause concern.[330]

Biological time-bomb ticks on

One of the other problems with medical treatments is that side-effects can take decades to appear, by which time it can be too late to prevent human tragedy. A well-known example is what happened to 10,000 women in the UK and 2,000,000 women in the USA who received a drug called diethylstilboestrol (DES) in an attempt to reduce miscarriages and premature birth. The drug was found to be useless. However, a hidden disaster occurred.

Some twenty years later it was realised that a generation of girls in their late teens and early twenties were developing vaginal and cervical cancers in much larger numbers than expected. At first the cause was a mystery until it was realised that daughters whose mothers had taken DES during pregnancy were up to 1,000 times more likely to develop the cancers. In addition, it emerged that congenital malformations had occurred in four out of ten of such children, often involving internal female reproductive organs, so only coming to light years after drug use by the mothers. The full scale of the disaster is still emerging, with reports that these young adults are themselves experiencing difficulties in pregnancy and a higher than normal incidence of depression and anxiety.[331]

A recent report concludes that 'the toxic time-bomb lives on . . . the history of DES underlines again that drugs and other treatments should not be widely used until their efficacy and safety are established'[332]—words particularly relevant to those wishing to use gene therapy widely, or to reprogram germ line cells with unknown implications for all subsequent generations.

2. Germ warfare using new organisms

Germ warfare research has been carried out in secret for decades. The first case of germ warfare in action was in the seige of Kaffa in the Crimea, Ukraine in 1347. Monguls hurled the bodies of plague victims over the city walls of the Genoese defenders. Genoese sailors carried the bacillus to European ports, accelerating the epidemic known as the Black Death.[333]

In the 1980s the world was shocked by the assassination of two well-known Bulgarian dissidents, one in Paris and the other in London. Both were killed in an identical way. A special umbrella was used by someone following them. In each case a tiny metal pellet was fired into the leg of the person just a metre or so in front. It felt like an insect bite. Neither realised much had happened until a few hours later when the wax coating on the pellet dissolved and an unknown biological weapon began to leak out of microscopic holes in the pellet surface. Within hours each was in hospital dying.

Germs to kill only the enemy

The fearsome spectre of germ weapons being used on a large scale on the battlefield was raised by the Gulf War in early 1991, when it was realised that Iraq possessed huge amounts of anthrax spores which could be spread over the desert using shells or helicopters, rendering large areas dangerous to humans.

Anthrax spores survive for many years under normal conditions. In the 1940s the small Scottish island Gruinard near Ullapool on the West coast became totally uninhabitable for fifty years, following experimental release of anthrax spores on the island to see how effective they would be in germ warfare. The island can now be visited without danger, but only because of a laborious manual and chemical clean-up operation. The UK continues to invest in ever more sophisticated germ weapons research at Porton Down just outside Salisbury.

The Gulf War also threatened civilians in the UK with germ warfare. In fact the risk of deliberate contamination of water supplies was considered so serious, according to an unconfirmed report, that a secret directive was issued to water treatment plants, doubling normal chlorine levels and asking them to exercise the utmost caution. While this would not have prevented the effects of many agents, it was hoped the chlorine might have reacted with added substances in a way which alerted staff to sabotage.[334]

Genetic engineering gives horrifying new powers to those who make such weapons. How about designing a new killer virus that produces death or severe illness in all those exposed to it in less than a week? At the same time, of course, all the troops on your own side are fully protected by giving them a special vaccine.

The 'best' virus type would be one which can be spread to a large number of people easily in a fine mist or in the water supply, but which does not pass easily from person to person, so the infection is contained in an area. For example, a fine mist of smallpox virus from a single helicopter in a single attack would be deadly to an unprotected army, but could also create a disaster across a whole continent. The agent needs to be very carefully engineered. Researchers are also developing biotech body suits: these are made of material impregnated with genetically engineered organisms designed to attack and neutralise germ warfare organisms or substances.[335]

Any volunteers?

Germ warfare is notoriously difficult to test—after all, who is going to volunteer for testing? Viruses are usually limited to one species, so you cannot reliably test new viral weapons on animals if the purpose is to kill humans. Viruses can also have unpredictable effects on large groups. Every time someone is infected, there is a new chance of a mutation or adaptation. The wider a virus spreads, the more likely it is to change— either becoming more dangerous or less harmful. New viruses would therefore be difficult to control, although that might not deter a dictator wishing to harass or intimidate a hated minority group in a sparsely occupied area.

Biological agents made by secret weapons research laboratories are of course tested—for without testing you have no weapon. Where and on whom such tests are being carried out is uncertain. All that is certain is that future tests are unlikely to be carried out on volunteers who know what is really being done, nor will they be conducted in lawsuit and media-dominated Western nations. What will be the results of the tests, and who will be given the information? Could a dangerous experiment involving a few people cause a strange new illness to spread out of control?

Strange new illnesses

It is obvious that mistakes could happen and doubtless we will see unexplained new diseases appearing in small groups from time to time before hopefully disappearing again. We may never know the true cause. After all, the secret service of a country is hardly likely to admit to trying out germ warfare on humans of another country in peacetime—or even during a full-scale war.

Other ways of using germs to fight wars include targeting viruses at the crops or animals that the enemy depends on for food. Here the testing is very straightforward and can be carried out in the animal houses of any of the major biological warfare research centres. Again, there is the potential for things to go very badly wrong.

Germ warfare by terrorists

Germ warfare is an attractive terrorist option, not just something to use in all-out war. After all, it is hard to prove or disprove whether a terrorist is bluffing, or whether what he or she says is about to be done is true. Because germ agents are unseen, a tiny amount of agent has the potential to terrorise and disrupt the lives of millions. Imagine the terrorist who telephones a national newspaper to say that ten phials of nerve agents or hazardous viruses will be added to one of the thousands of distribution points of our domestic water supply. Over 30,000,000 adults would be boiling all drinking water for weeks—especially if one or two had died already.

The next century is perhaps more likely to be dominated by terrorism than major wars. The collapse of the Eastern Bloc has already produced a number of independent states or countries in which conflicts similar to those in Northern Ireland are developing, even to the point of full-scale civil war. These conflicts have often arisen as a result of large-scale people movements, so that many nations now have sizeable groups within them who have very different cultures and identities.

While some countries cope well and are enriched by diversity, others are becoming increasingly torn apart by different communities who feel their identities and interests are being threatened. Tribalism, or fierce loyalty to a social group, is a very powerful force at almost every level in every society. Tribalism is often the glue holding people together, but its exclusive nature can also drive people apart. We see it at football matches, in factories, in families, on housing estates, in political parties and in church denominations. We also see it in ethnic tensions and armed conflict.

Apart from integration and toleration, partition is often seen as the only other solution for a troubled nation. This happened in India in the 1940s creating the new states of Pakistan and Bangladesh. When partition occurred, tens of thousands of people fled from one side to the other. Life is never neat and tidy. Partition usually fails, or results in terrible bloodshed and persecution, because every town or village contains a variable mixture, increasing pressures for the horrors of 'ethnic cleansing'.

Every major war between countries over the last forty years has produced large numbers of refugees: people on the move and looking for sanctuary. Political upheavals and instability also add to the chaos. In addition, there are also many very positive reasons for people to move and settle in other countries, a process encouraged by relaxation of border controls, multi-national co-operation and high speed travel.

The end result is that the world is steadily becoming more muddled. This can be a good thing in producing large cosmopolitan multi-nation cities such as London, but can also be the seed-bed for resentment, anger, oppression and protests, all feeding the growth of new terrorist groups likely to be interested in the fearsome powers of germ warfare.

A dictator's dream

Germ warfare is also an attractive option for state control—particularly in a totalitarian state that wishes over a generation to reduce vastly the size and influence of a certain minority community without outside interference. There are many ways in which genetic engineering could help. For example, a special bogus immunisation programme could be set up for all children in a particular region. The vaccine could be deliberately contaminated with an extra virus which has an identical surface appearance to the outside coating of human sperm.

After the symptomless infection has been eliminated, each person will be vaccinated not only against the virus, but also against human sperm. All the boys will carry antibodies for the rest of their lives that recognise human sperm as germs to be destroyed. This auto-immune reaction will make them sterile for life.[336] Such cross-reactions between infections are well known and are the basis for most of the auto-immune diseases that we discussed in the last chapter.

A super-race

Another dictator's dream might be to produce a super-race. The idea of selective breeding to improve the human species was first proposed by Francis Galton in 1883 and was known as 'eugenics'. In 1895 the ideas were put to work by a group from Germany who sailed to Paraguay to set up a Pure Arian Republic. The colony still exists today, sustained by extreme exclusivism.

Negative eugenics was practised by Hitler, as the elimination of 'defective genes' from a population by preventing groups intermarrying or even by mass murder. Hitler's dream was of a master race with superior intelligence and physical attractiveness. Just consider for a moment what disasters would have followed had gene modification and cloning been available to him fifty years ago.

Every decade produces its own batch of dictators, some more terrible than others. Gene technology offers the dictator of today vastly greater powers to alter the genes of a nation than at any time in human history. Without ethical constraints, progress in human research involving embryos and foetuses could be very rapid. Compared to the huge industry needed for atomic weapons development, the equipment needed to start gene modifications or cloning is neither bulky nor particularly expensive.

Controlling sex

There are other social consequences of genetic engineering. We already have techniques capable of guaranteeing couples an 80% chance of producing the sex of their choice.[337] With families becoming smaller, such choices may create great sex imbalances for the future.[338] We know the catastrophic events that followed the Chinese decree some years ago that only one child was to be permitted per family: very large numbers of baby girls were murdered at birth because for cultural reasons it was important to most families that their only child was a son. There is now a long-term shortage of girls in some areas. This is likely to have vast social consequences felt for the next two generations.

A survey of couples in New York showed that USA citizens tended to choose boys and girls equally, but all fifty-seven of the non-American interviewed selected boys for economic and business reasons (40%), cultural reasons (30%) and personal reasons (30%).[339] Clearly if this technology becomes inexpensive and widely available there could be a major effect on the balance of sexes in some countries.

There are other ways in which the balance of sexes could be profoundly altered. For example, a combination of existing cloning techniques and surrogacy could allow in theory an entirely female group, society or nation to be made.

3. Food safety

We have already looked at the large range of new foods about to appear, or already available, and the absence of adequate control mechanisms to ensure gene products are not sold without full safety testing. Such testing will never be applied thoroughly without some kind of global regulatory authority, which is very unlikely—not least of all because the resources required to test transgenic livestock, for example, will be much greater than those needed to create them.[340] We will be looking in detail at the issue of regulations in the next chapter.

4. Abuse of genetically created medicines

Parental pressure and expectations for the achievements of their children can produce demands for misuse of gene technology. An example might be pressure to prescribe human growth hormone to children of shorter than average parents to encourage development of a taller athletic adult. A recent survey of paediatricians in France showed great concern about risks of inappropriate use.[341] The main medical indication for its use is to treat human dwarfism, although athletes are already abusing it to try and improve performance.[342]

Abuse of gene screening

Before long it may be possible to predict the intelligence of a child from the genetic profile of a foetus just weeks after conception. Dr Robert Goodman of the Institute of Psychiatry in London believes this may be possible in five to ten years. A recent article in the *Independent* said:

> Before very long, parents who want to get their son into Eton may find they have to submit the genetic profile of the foetus just weeks after conception. Other parents may try to abort foetuses until they

conceive one that prenatal tests indicate has what they think is the right combination of intelligence genes. One only has to look at how much some parents are willing to spend on private schools in the hope of increasing their children's educational attainments . . . it may be possible for them to attain the same end at lower cost through selective abortion guided by even relatively imprecise genetic predictions.[343]

We do not yet know how many genes are responsible for intelligence. If just five genes are responsible together for around half the variation, then it is very likely that we will be able to test for them within ten years. The same could apply to other areas of personality and physical performance.

A world without pain?

Here is a thought-provoking extract from a paper published in a scientific journal in March 1990, looking forward to a genetically engineered world without pain—not one that is practical, as we will see, but challenging the way we see our future nevertheless:

> Riley-Day Syndrome, a genetic disorder in which there is an impaired ability or inability to feel pain, hot and cold, is . . . evidence that the . . . notion that life cannot be painless is not necessarily valid.
> . . . a mind capable of experiencing only varying degrees of pleasure . . . the human brain would be rendered painless [with a] genetic approach. In order to expedite the relief of all kinds of suffering and the improvement of the human condition in general . . . prompt and concerted research should be directed towards the development of such a brain. . . .[344]

Use or abuse of genetic research? If it is any reassurance to you, the author fails to point out that people unable to experience pain do not tend to last very long without terrible injuries or even death. Pain is a biological protective device to tell you when things are being damaged. Not only are burns and cuts very common, but we also see a higher than usual rate of joint problems such as arthritis—even in the very young. The reason seems to be that we all need subtle posture changes all the time to keep our tissues from being worn out or damaged.

While I have been typing this chapter I have probably altered my position a few times without realising it to keep comfortable in the pre-pain stage.

In conclusion we have seen that gene technology, while having the capacity to revolutionise our lives, also has the power to destroy us and to devastate our planet. The promise of massive benefits and huge commercial gain means gene changes will continue to be developed quickly—possibly with little regard for public safety, the environment or ethics. In the light of this we need to ask what controls there are, and whether they are enough.

9
Controlling Gene Technology

Preparing for the future

Now we have seen the breathtaking power of gene technology, we need to consider urgently some of the issues involved. There are two main questions we need to ask about each area of gene modification. First, is the technology properly regulated by law so that it is safe? Secondly, is the use of the technology always right?[345] In this chapter we are going to consider safety issues primarily, in the context of current regulations.

Is gene modification safe?

We have looked in detail at the risks from gene modification in the previous chapter. However, there is a real danger of an instant response based on emotion and fear rather than reason and common sense. The first thing that is obvious is that there are a number of processes which are merely direct extensions of long established practices, such as cross-breeding and propagating plants using cuttings, or giving medicines to alter the way human cells behave, or transplanting organs from one person to another. In medicine, some doctors are concerned that public debates on safety of gene modifications in general could cause an over-reaction, and possible rejection, of life-saving gene therapy for serious genetic disease.[346]

However, as we have seen, there are a large number of new

areas where massive strides forward are being made with very little control, particularly in the areas of food production, environmental release of altered species, viral contamination and spread, and biological warfare research.

Public right to know

Very few people realise the extent and speed of the genetic revolution. Many find the terminology confusing and difficult to understand. Those at the forefront of developing new gene products are often worried about public reaction, so little publicity is sought. Research papers are usually published a long time after the research is finished and can be a poor guide to what is happening today or what is planned for tomorrow. A few scientists experimenting beyond ethical boundaries may be tempted to publish only what they are happy for others to learn about, so the most sensitive 'unofficial' experiments may be unreported.

Almost all sources of public information about gene modification come from the very people who have the most to lose from regulations, not just in terms of scientific freedom, but also commercial gain. A number of gene engineers, especially in the USA, have huge commercial interests in the application of their work. For example, one Nobel prize winner, Herb Boyer, invested $500 to help launch Genentech. When the company was floated in October 1980 his stake was worth $82 million.[347] This is why some are concerned that risks may be played down, that accidents may be kept very quiet and that experiments likely to trouble the public conscience may be done quietly, without necessarily publishing results.

An example of secrecy has been over the testing of growth hormone in cows. The milk-boosting bovine somatotrophin (BST) can increase milk yields by 20%. Developed by Monsanto, Eli Lilly, Upjohn and American Cyanamid, BST was on secret trial in the UK for four years, with milk produced entering the dairies and being sold for public use (see page 86).

Lessons from irradiation of food

The food industry is one where there is great consumer sensitivity—especially in the West—with an increasing emphasis on 'natural' foods. An example was the huge consumer reaction seen recently over the proposed introduction of food irradiation. The technique involves blasting pre-packaged foods with a large dose of X-ray radiation. The doses used are enough to kill any bacteria, so the food inside the sealed packet becomes effectively sterile.

At first there were natural anxieties about whether any surviving organisms might be likely to mutate into a more dangerous form. That fear has been largely laid to rest by extensive tests which show these germs cannot survive the process. The next fear was that the treatment would be used to sterilise decaying or contaminated food which would then be sold in supermarkets having been passed as safe.

Public fear leads to caution

The simple fact is that people are afraid of radiation. They think of nuclear bombs or such things as the contamination of Welsh sheep by the Chernobyl nuclear disaster in the former Soviet Union. Radiation to the public means only one thing: irreversible contamination with invisible particles which cause cancer and kill.

Irradiation of food is probably completely safe, and would doubtless have been in wide use by now if food manufacturers had been able to introduce the technique without any publicity. Instead, after big media coverage and public pressure from consumer groups, manufacturers were forced to indicate on the labelling if radiation was used. The regulation killed the process stone dead as far as many suppliers were concerned.

Unless there is a regulation, you and I will continue to discover we have been buying genetically engineered foods after we have eaten them rather than before. Who wants to advertise the fact and risk a massive loss in sales?

In the meantime, consumer pressure is growing in the USA for 'anti-advertising' promoted by the Pure Food Campaign. Already some 1,500 top chefs in America have agreed to display the Campaign's logo bearing the words 'We do not serve genetically engineered foods.'[348]

The European response

So what response should there be to gene technology? First, we have to be realistic. I am very doubtful about the ability of any single government or group of governments to control it effectively—even if they agree to do so. Nevertheless, there are important steps which can be taken which will have some impact on the greatest risks, and will provide some ethical constraints.

Let us look first of all at how governments have been responding. On 23rd April 1990 the Council of the European Communities issued two key directives.[349] The first covered use of organisms in controlled (contained) situations, and the other covered environmental release. Each country was asked to approve national legislation by October 1991 at the latest. However, only Denmark had done so even by early 1992. One reason for delay has been the great difficulty in wording legislation so it is clear, unambiguous, satisfactory to worried members of the public and relaxed enough to encourage massive commercial investment.

Current UK controls

In the UK, current legislation comes mainly under the Health and Safety at Work Act for people, and under the Environment Protection Act. The UK has had a long history of voluntary monitoring—since 1978 genetic activities have been reported routinely under Health and Safety guidelines, updated into regulations in 1989. A major consultation exercise began in October 1991 to try to devise one set of regulations to cover both health and safety, and environment, with one set of inspectors to enforce them managed by Health and Safety.

The UK has taken the view that there is no enormous urgency because so many aspects of genetic engineering are already covered in one way or another by existing laws, regulations or voluntary reporting systems. However, such a position may be seriously flawed. In particular all voluntary reporting systems are likely to be ignored by some—particularly by those whose work is on the outer edges of what is acceptable.

1. Consumer safety

Existing UK law covers certain genetically engineered products. For example, cosmetics and cleaning materials made using biotechnology are covered by the 1987 Consumer Protection Act. Under this Act the Secretary of State can first seek voluntary action by a supplier, failing which prohibition notices may be issued. Emergency regulations can be activated for a year to cover more general hazards.

Under the Act anyone injured by a defective product, whether sold to them or not, can sue manufacturers, importers or suppliers for damages, without having to prove negligence. Suppliers are only liable if they fail to identify the producer, importer or own-brand supplier. Under the Act it is a criminal offence to supply any consumer product which is unsafe.[350]

2. Patents

Under UK law, microbiological processes are patentable, as are micro-organisms, if special procedures are required to obtain them. Thus, in principle, there is no bar on obtaining a patent for micro-organisms including viruses, processes for producing micro-organisms, processes using micro-organisms, cell lines in culture, and for products obtained from microbiological processes. However, breeding of animals or plant propagation not requiring advanced technology cannot be stopped by a patent, thus preserving ancient plant and animal breeding rights for farmers.[351]

This patent loophole is of great concern to the gene industry because it means in theory the entire world sales of a new genetically engineered plant or animal might only be a single seed or just one embryo. From then on the farming community could legally reproduce their own free samples, bankrupting the research company.

3. Health and safety

Health and safety of workers involved in gene modification are covered under the 1974 Health and Safety at Work Act, and under the 1988 Control of Substances Hazardous to Health Regulations. The 1989 Genetic Manipulation Regulations require notification to the Health and Safety Executive (HSE) of intention to carry out genetic modifications. Each centre carrying out work is required to set up a local genetic manipulation safety subcommittee.

If work involves organisms known to be dangerous, such as the Lassa and Marburg viruses, then notification is also required under the Health and Safety (dangerous pathogens) Regulations passed in 1981.[352]

4. Genetically engineered medicines

Genetically engineered medicines are covered by the same regulations as all other new medicinal products, and must gain approval by the UK Licensing Authority. Companies must also obtain a manufacturing licence.[353]

5. Food safety

The main legislation covering food for human consumption in the UK is the Food Safety Act which became law in January 1991. Under the Act it is an offence to render any food injurious to health by adding any articles or substance, or by subjecting the food to any process or treatment.[354]

The Food Safety Act contains specific powers that could be used to regulate genetically engineered foodstuffs. Submissions are made to the Advisory Committee on Novel Foods and Processes which was established in a new structure in 1988.[355] However, the companies are under no obligation to tell the committee anything. The process is entirely voluntary.[356]

(a) Food labelling

The above committee considers there is probably a need for labelling of foods containing genetically modified organisms, or trans-species where the species contains genetic material from another plant, animal or other organism. At the moment each case is being considered 'on its own merits'. If labelling is considered appropriate, it is likely to be: '. . . contains products of gene technology'.[357]

This committee is the same one in origin as the one which handled the question of food irradiation. Following massive consumer reaction to irradiation, suppliers are hardly likely to be enthusiastic about labelling their products as genetically engineered.

Since the whole reporting system is run on a voluntary basis, there is no regulatory or legal power to force companies to tell the committee about new vegetable types or animal variants they intend to sell to wholesalers. A company could always argue after the event that it had acted in good faith and had inadvertently overlooked normal procedures.

Wholesalers may say they imported certain fruits and vegetables in good faith, believing they were natural strains, being identical outwardly, just lower cost. The hidden reason for low cost might be special genetic properties such as internal production of insecticides.

(b) Pesticides

Under the Control of Pesticides Regulations 1986 no pesticide, including biological agents, can be sold in the UK without approval, involving extensive laboratory tests.[358] There are time limits forbidding farmers to use these agents near to harvest time. New types of plants with built-in genetic resistance to pests are covered. These plants could be producing levels of insecticide toxic to humans. However, evasion of regulations may be hard to detect.

6. Plant Breeders' Rights

Under the 1978 Plant Breeders' Rights legislation, farmers are allowed to retain seed from a crop to sow next year, without legal action by the original supplier of the strain of cereal. The same freedom applies to other plant and animal stock. National and international discussions are taking place to try to find a compromise allowing breeders to maintain their rights, while providing licensing arrangements to protect manufacturers of genetically engineered varieties.[359]

7. Environment

At present the Health and Safety Executive is notified regarding virus releases into the environment. Introduction of new species, such as genetically engineered caterpillars, may be covered under the Wildlife and Countryside Act. This is one of the most important areas to regulate, and one of the weakest at the moment.

A new government approach

The 1990 EC directives are wide ranging and specific, especially regarding the control of environmental releases of genetically modified organisms. As a response, the UK Health and Safety Commission consultation paper of October 1991 proposed new regulations.[360] The paper runs to almost 200 pages of highly technical detail, all aimed at preserving the balance between the public right to impose safety, information and ethical constraints, and the right of industry to freely develop commercial products without constant red tape, restriction, extra cost and legal disputes.

The key questions are these: Who has won? Is the proposed compromise between polarised interests a good one? Is any compromise on safety, information and ethical constraints acceptable to the public? Has there been adequate public debate? Is the document itself simple enough for members of the public to understand?

The answer is that it is difficult to tell who has won. There has been little or no public debate and the original version of the document itself was very technical and hard to understand. Environmentalists say the Department of the Environment has caved in to the demands of industry, with added confidentiality clauses meaning that companies can withhold the locations of trials, and information on 'anything that might prejudice the patentability of a genetically modified organism'. If this is interpreted widely, it could enable companies to continue to be very secretive.

Some are worried that the whole tone of the legislation has changed from a strict and by-the-letter interpretation of the EC directives to something that seeks to reassure industry. For example, companies are now to be allowed to get one consent at the start of a whole development programme covering several sites and many organisms over five to ten years.

On the other hand, industry experts have warned that if earlier proposals had become law, many companies would have moved to other countries where regulations are more relaxed. They point to the rapid exodus of investment, companies and research talent from Germany following new regulations.[361] They say secrecy is essential to protect investment from theft, copying or sabotage.

Fields of growing crops are very vulnerable to damage by protesters, as recent events in Denmark showed when a group of activists cut down a field of genetically modified maize, destroying £600,000 of investment, and setting back research by at least a year. This was the second year running that the same company had been targeted. The company is now considering a move to a country where they can keep locations of trials secret.[362]

It is not surprising that investors are becoming scared. In 1989 venture capital organisations in Europe invested £101 million in biotechnology, but in 1991 the amount had fallen to only £67 million. In Britain the investment fell from £35 million to £15 million in the same period. Meanwhile, investment is growing rapidly in the Far East where controls are less strict.[363]

Conflict between profit, progress and public concern

The drive to develop new genetically engineered products is huge and pressures are growing to be increasingly soft on regulations for the sake of the future health of the economy. As with the microchip revolution, the UK is keen to have a big slice of the action as the world gene trade booms. Some have argued that having too many regulations could rob the whole European Community of the best scientists, discoveries and commercial benefits.

Companies want assurances that if they invest massively in gene products they will not later find themselves up against the same wall of bureaucracy they have already found in Germany. In the USA there have been moves recently to loosen up regulation after fears that regulations were forcing massive research investments out of the country. This is a spectacular U-turn in the battle between 'green' consumers and big business. The only answer is to agree the same regulations in many different countries.

So how big is the research machine and commercial backing? It is thought by the government that in the UK alone around 400 centres are currently involved in genetic modifications, including university projects and industrial laboratories. Two British biotech companies are particularly well established and are about to float on the US stock exchange: Cantab Pharmaceuticals based in Cambridge and British Biotechnology based in Oxford. Celltech and Xenova hope to follow soon.[364]

The dominant government influencers are the Department of Trade and Industry and the Ministry of Agriculture, Fisheries and Food. Both are concerned primarily with assisting producers rather than representing health, safety or environmental concerns. Balance in legislation, and the way in which regulations are actually implemented on a day-to-day basis, depends therefore on the key roles of other government departments responsible for Health and Environment.

Department of Trade and Industry

A key influence in the Department of Trade and Industry (DTI) is the Interdepartmental Committee on Biotechnology (ICBT). This was set up under the chairmanship of the Government Chemist in April 1982 to 'provide a focus for biotechnology in government and stimulate its development'. It co-ordinates the work of the DTI (lead department with overall responsibility for encouraging industrial application of new technology for the maximum benefit of UK industry) and other departments and agencies covering areas such as health, safety, environment, agriculture, food and research.

The Department of Trade and Industry aims 'to create a climate that stimulates enterprise and reduces red tape'.[365] Its specialist biotechnology department is called the Biotechnology Unit, a key aim of which is to 'improve the environment for investment in biotechnology through balanced regulations and public perception, supported by adequate risk assessment'.[366]

Massive government investment

LINK investment programmes (50% matched government funding) totalling £65.35 million have been approved over three to five years.[367] Around forty universities and eighty industrial groups are involved in LINK projects. Some of the projects are listed:

1. Food Processing Sciences Programme:
   * Genetic engineering of food micro-organisms.
   £14 million over five years.
2. Biotransformation Programme:
   * Further development of methods to enhance use of biotransformation.
   £4 million over four years.
3. Eukaryotic Genetic Engineering Programme:
   * Genetic methods for identification of genes which code important proteins.
   * Development of new ways of reprogramming cells.
   * Identification of control mechanisms that modulate the expression of genes.
   * Efficient activation of newly added genes.
   * Transfer between species of traits associated with gene complexes.
   £5.2 million over four years.

An associated scheme is called EUREKA: a framework for collaborative research projects involving eighteen European countries. Support of up to 50% is available for UK participants.[368]

In addition, the Agricultural and Food Research Council (AFRC) allocated over £24 million in 1989/90 to a range of genetic modification projects covering:

* Production of medically important proteins such as insulin, alpha-1 antitrypsin (to treat emphysema[369]) and blood coagulation factors in the milk of sheep or cattle.

* Development of transgenic animals to study the role of genes in development.
* Improvement in nutrition, growth, lactation and reproduction through the use of modified micro-organisms, feed additives, in-vitro fertilisation and embryo transfer.
* Improvement of consumer appeal of plants.
* Development of plants with low requirements for pesticides, fungicides or fertiliser.

New government proposals

While the agencies listed above are pushing research ahead as fast as possible, and are doing all they can to encourage British companies to get involved in modifying genes, the Departments of Health and Environment are seeking to impose constraint.

New proposals will require that most work on genetic modification should be notified. Some activities will require formal consent—all releases of products for example. Once consent is given by one EC country—a process involving consultation with other EC members—then approval will be automatic throughout the EC.

Future applications to bring new products to market will require sending a summary proposal from a manufacturer to the European Commission. Each member state will then be sent a copy for comment. Final approval will be formally granted by the country first approached on behalf of the whole community.

Exploiting a 'weak link'

In theory a company could choose to bring in a gene product via the 'weakest link', or the country which seemed most likely to have a relaxed attitude. Backdoor importation of biotechnology could easily occur since the national government first approached will always have the dominant say in that particular licence approval.

An EC company operating in one country might then decide to apply for a licence in another. UK companies involved in controversial research may choose to relocate outside the EC altogether, only bothering to approach licensing authorities with finished products. Locating laboratories in developing countries may also be some protection against industrial espionage and theft of cultures—one test-tube can contain the products of millions of pounds of investment.

Applications may not always be scrutinised closely by each country. The advisory panels in most countries are staffed by busy scientists with their own heavy research workloads. Therefore civil servants are reluctant to load them with unnecessary time-consuming licence applications.[370]

Difficult to draft effective gene laws

In any event, whatever laws we propose we still face a big problem: laws need to be introduced and enforced globally to be effective. The problems in agreeing about what needs to be regulated are huge enough. However, the greatest difficulty of all is finding some good definitions that will close certain avenues effectively, while leaving others open.[371]

A recent example of chaos was what happened in Australia following implementation of the Infertility (Medical Procedures) Act in 1987, designed to outlaw 'cloning'. This was meant to prevent human cloning experiments like those we looked at in Chapter 3. However, it also effectively banned the cloning of individual human cells—nothing short of disastrous. Monoclonal antibodies (see p 106) were in danger of becoming illegal for a start. Calls have therefore been made to amend the Act.[372]

Having highlighted the huge gaps in international law, and in current or proposed UK regulations, we need to look hard at the most difficult and agonising area of all. Is gene technology and research always right—or should some approaches or techniques be abandoned?

10

When Is Gene Technology Right or Wrong?

Common principles

Having considered some urgent issues relating to the safety of this new technology, we now need to turn to a much more difficult and sensitive area to ask whether the areas of activity we have looked at in earlier chapters are morally right, wrong, or neutral. Broadly speaking, these questions need to be applied to two main areas: the development of humans from egg to embryo to birth; and the radical changing of species.

Each of us has a view of the world which will colour our response to these things—and I have my own. However, it is helpful first to establish a few common principles that most people would probably accept.

(a) The monster principle

The first common principle is an aesthetic dislike of creating the grossly unnatural, or monsters. In the travelling fairs of some countries you can enter a tent for a small charge and see some of the strange wonders of the world: animals with two heads stuffed in a glass box, or a baby with two heads and four arms. The Elephant Man of the last century was not a loved or popular public figure—but he attracted crowds. Going to the zoo to see cages full of animals artificially mutated beyond all recognition may or may not turn out to be a money-spinner for the owners, but most of us would agree that to seek to create

165

such creatures deliberately, for curiosity or profit, would be wrong.

(b) The human principle

The second common principle is a strong sense of what a human being is—we recognise other human beings instinctively without necessarily being able to analyse all the reasons why. Our whole civilisation rests on social interaction and respect between individuals and groups of people. Therefore, a language-speaking chimpanzee with reasoning powers, will, personality and artistic ability, is likely to be disturbing to most—especially if the chimpanzee talks fluently, with a large vocabulary, dresses in human clothes and adopts human mannerisms. The issue of humanity is also an issue touching on spirituality.

When it is realised that the cause of this unexpected genius is a simple insertion of human genes into a monkey embryo, there may well be some who begin to wonder if the creature is not in fact more human than animal. After all, many owners of pets have similar feelings of identity with their dogs or cats. I think there is a huge natural curiosity about such human-animal possibilities, but a common revulsion against the thought of having to live with the consequences on a daily basis.

A personal view

However, once we go beyond these basic areas of intuitive agreement we can quickly land up in a sea without any bearings or boundaries at all. I am going to share a personal view—not necessarily thinking that you will agree with me, but partly to throw into sharper focus what you yourself are comfortable or uncomfortable with.

My own reactions have been very much influenced by the experimental approach to science we were given at Cambridge, where no 'fact' was ever taught without describing the experiments and the results on which this understanding was based, and then by my experience completing medical training and practising as a doctor. My thinking has also been influenced by Christian faith. So as this book has developed, I have been asking what a Christian view should be on genetic modification, paying particular attention to principles from my understanding of the Bible.

As I have gathered the material you have read, gleaned from sources in many countries of the world, I have at times been stopped in my tracks. Sometimes it has been surprise at some remarkable piece of research, or new information that changed my perspective. However, at other times I have had to stop and think, not about what I had read, but about what lay between the lines.

The very next chapter in this rapidly developing story seems likely to contain huge unimaginable consequences for our future world. I have often wondered what else will have happened by the time the book is updated for a second edition. I am sure you too have reacted quite strongly to some of the information contained in this book. Some things you may have found hard to accept or believe and will have dismissed, while other things will have seemed too near and too real for comfort and will have been deeply disturbing.

The mystery of life—and death

I am sure that most doctors with experience of caring for the dying find that their respect for human life continues to increase over the years. There is an amazing mystery here which one is reluctant to tamper with. Having been present during the birth of all four of our children, and at the death of many people, I feel privileged to have witnessed profoundly moving events. The existence of an added dimension is particularly obvious to me when caring for those who are dying.

Caring for those with AIDS

In 1987 Gerald Coates and others in Pioneer encouraged me to write a book about how the church should respond to the AIDS epidemic, *The Truth About AIDS*. The first print-run sold out in months and other editions followed. As a direct result, a new AIDS initiative was born in 1988 called ACET (AIDS Care Education and Training). It was set up as a national and international Christian response to the AIDS epidemic, providing homecare and prevention programmes here in the UK and overseas. ACET uses volunteers extensively alongside professional staff to provide whatever is needed for someone ill or dying with AIDS to stay at home. ACET is involved in supporting several hundred people ill with HIV or AIDS at home in the UK at any one time.

A life-changing experience

To be present for the first time at the moment of death can be a life-changing experience. However much training and preparation have been given, nothing can take away from the full impact of the event itself. Perhaps for several hours the person has been very weak and sleepy—although orientated and able to talk if roused by a visitor. Maybe for the last hour or two the carer has noticed how the breathing pattern has gradually changed and the pulse is becoming weaker. It seems at times that his breathing is about to fade away altogether.

Eventually the carer becomes aware that the breathing has finally stopped. The house is quiet and still. The person dying is still there—whatever they say, death is far from instant. After a further minute or two there is another sharp intake of breath and then all is still again. Being present and involved at such a time is a special privilege and leaves a deep impression.

Something is missing

Here is an individual bounded in space and time, usually full of vitality, personality and fun. Just an hour or two ago he had been very much alive, but now he is gone. His skin cells are still alive. His heart muscle is still alive. His gut is still digesting food and his bone marrow is still producing red blood cells. Almost all the cells in his body will continue to live if they are removed quite soon and if they are cared for appropriately. But he himself has gone. All the chemicals, proteins, sugars and gases are still present in each cell—but something is missing. The conscious, caring, laughing, crying individual person has gone, with echoes left vividly in the memory and reminders of his life and personality all around the room.

More to Life than life

This mystery has had a profound effect on the way I view life. There is more to Life than life. You and I are more than the sum of our constituent parts. There is more to human consciousness and individuality than just a bunch of chemicals or a set of genes. There is more to it than just a complex bio-machine driven by a few long strips of genetic code.

This mystery is seen again in the study of how a single fertilised egg develops so rapidly, so predictably and so perfectly into a whole new being which is then born into the world. Trillions of cells from just one in only nine months, increasing in total mass by six billion times. I find myself compelled to take human life seriously, to resist the temptation to medical heroics when someone is reaching the end, and to be very cautious indeed about interfering with someone's beginning. Of course faith adds another dimension, but this sensitivity to human life is independent of faith.

Christians believe that human beings were made in the image of God,[373] and are uniquely different from other species, as conscious, creative, physical and spiritual beings, capable of making moral choices. We have been commanded to 'fill the earth and subdue it . . . [ruling] over every living creature' as custodians of God's creation.[374] In the light of this, what sense can we make of genetic engineering?

First we understand that the use of science to harness the positive potential of the world God has given us is entirely as God intended. Secondly, we realise our responsibility to take care of God's world. Thirdly, we recognise that human life has a spiritual dimension and is therefore to be treated as a sacred mystery, with the utmost respect.[375]

Cloning destroys individuality

In the light of these things I am opposed to human cloning that produces identical twins where the twins will be born either at different times, or to different parents. Cloning by definition robs people of individuality, and creating clones to provide spare parts for others is particularly abhorrent in the way it devalues human life.

Choosing boys or girls can affect a nation

I am seriously concerned about the widespread availability of choosing the sex of children—even if it does not involve the selective destruction of rejected embryos, but is achieved by separating sperm in the laboratory. I do not trust society to make sure there continues to be a proper balance between the sexes. As we have seen, in many countries the result could be a gross imbalance between men and women, with terrible social consequences.

I can see that parents who have had three boys and really want a girl, or the other way round, may want to use science to guarantee the sex of their next baby. Parents with evidence of a sex-linked gene defect such as that causing haemophilia are particularly likely to want to determine the sex of their children to ensure that only girls are conceived for health reasons. This is quite a different situation from choosing the sex of a child simply on the basis of personal preference; no different perhaps from choosing a child on the basis of its musical or athletic genes—a hazardous path.

Pre-birth screening dilemmas

The issue of pre-natal diagnosis is less easy than many Christians think. There are many different views on the status of the fertilised egg, the embryo and the developing foetus, even among those who would say they are Christians. Some hold the view that from the moment of conception a human individual has come into being, while others take the view that the true humanity of the developing organism is something that increases or alters with time. There are infinite variations in shades of opinion on this emotive subject, even among those who would say they accept the Bible as their final authority.

My purpose here is not to alter the view you may have, but to explore some of the implications when we come to look at gene modification and the birth of babies. Some aspects of pre-birth screening have been going on for years and are a normal part of everyday medical practice. Doctors are faced with difficult, complex and agonising decisions which appear to defeat the cut-and-dried rulebook approach.

For example, mothers can be screened to see if they are immune to rubella (German measles). If not, they can be vaccinated prior to conception to avoid the possibility of infection in the first three months of pregnancy, which would have damaging results for the child. Screening during pregnancy can also avoid a rare but serious complication, where a particular immune response by the mother to the baby's red blood cells causes the baby to develop problems in the womb, or in severe cases to die before birth. Giving the mother specially prepared antibodies can prevent the problem.[376]

However, the most sensitive issue is the detection of genetic abnormalities for which there is as yet no genetic 'refit' possible. As we have seen, the range of diseases for which genetic screening of foetuses is possible is growing rapidly, whether for Down's syndrome, Tay Sachs disease, Thalassaemia, cystic fibrosis or other illnesses.[377]

Routine testing in the womb

These tests are being used routinely already. As a Christian couple, my wife and I were appalled to find we were being more or less told that blood taken while my wife attended the ante-natal clinic was going to be used among other things for genetic screening—in this instance to test for alpha-foetoprotein. The only purpose of the test would have been to approach us with the suggestion of an abortion if the test showed up a possible problem.[378] In fact, had my wife not objected, the test would have been carried out as a matter of routine.

The reason for the test is to detect if the baby is developing with a problem known as spina bifida. This is where the tissues forming part of the brain and spinal cord fail to form properly. They form first as a dark coloured strip on the outside of the embryo, running from the bottom of the back up to the head. This strip forms in a similar way in all mammals and has been studied extensively. It is known as the neural ridge or groove. In the malformed baby, part or all of this strip fails to roll up properly into a tube covered with skin.

Detecting spina bifida

When the baby is born, the part of the nervous tissue which is exposed to the outside world is quickly damaged. The severity of the condition can vary enormously from a pinhole at the base of the spine, which is so minor as to be missed by the midwife and doctor at birth, to a most severe malformation incompatible with life.

The blood test works by measuring the level of alpha-foetoprotein circulating in the mother's blood, which has been released by the abnormally exposed tissues in the womb and has then crossed the placenta into the mother.[379] A high level indicates a defect such as spina bifida, while a low level may indicate Down's syndrome.[380] Unfortunately, the blood test gives little or no indication of the severity of the condition, and can be unreliable. In one out of five cases the result will be normal, even if a defect is present. Sometimes the test can be positive, even if the child is normal. The test is usually done at around sixteen to eighteen weeks.

If an abnormality is suspected, an ultrasound scan is done, and a sample of the amniotic fluid surrounding the baby is taken and analysed. Amniocentesis can cause a miscarriage.[381] In addition, the result is wrong in up to fifteen out of a hundred cases. We must conclude therefore that every week in the UK some normal babies are aborted.[382]

A right to life?

But what if a child is not 'normal'? We chose not to have the test because we had already made a decision that any child of ours would live—even if it did not fit into our intolerant society's views of what 'normal' is. God values us for who we are, not for what we are able to do, and a genetic problem cannot affect how much he loves us.[383] What right have we to destroy another?

Therefore we would not welcome a massive increase in the number of conditions or tendencies to disease which could be routinely detected in blood tests offered to all pregnant women. Unfortunately, knowing trends in my own profession, I suspect that batteries of these tests will become as routine as testing for anaemia, and people will only find out after the event what tests were done when a doctor asks to see them about a worrying result.

The reason I say this is because such screening is standard practice in most other areas of medicine. For example, someone admitted with a range of unexplained symptoms may well have blood taken to be analysed for over a dozen different conditions. The doctor taking blood will probably comment, 'We are just checking your blood for any abnormalities and to make sure you are not anaemic.' A recent survey of 295 geneticists in the USA showed over 75% were in favour of carrying out pre-natal blood screening, even if the mother was not interested in having an abortion after the test.[384]

How big is a risk?

Even if you take the position, as many do, that in extreme cases of congenital malformations abortion is acceptable, where do you draw the line? How severe is severe? Some of these future tests might indicate, say, a twice than normal risk of breast cancer, or a doubled risk of a heart problem before the age of sixty-five.

We have looked earlier at the form of bowel cancer which is inherited with the polyposis gene. However, this type of bowel cancer is very rare compared to the main types. Overall, cancers of the large bowel (colo-rectal) are the third most common cancers worldwide. As our understanding of the different risk factors has grown, we have come to recognise that there may be a genetic component in a great many cases. The genetic change alone is not enough to form cancers without other nutritional factors as well, which may include fat, excess calories, the amount of fibre or calcium, selenium and various vitamins in the diet.[385]

A recent report on bowel cancer by the World Health Organisation says: 'Recent studies in genetic epidemiology and molecular biology have shown that inherited genetic factors play an important role in colorectal carcinogenesis. . . . Prevention . . . should therefore be [available] to all populations who are at risk because of dietary and hereditary predisposition.'[386] We will have a very long list of such mixed-cause diseases before long.

Pedigree humans for life insurance or jobs

Before we know where we are we could have begun a serious process of transforming the genetic pool of the human species, otherwise known as eugenics. Incidentally, if we were to do this extensively, then we would start to see other major problems from interbreeding. We would be developing a new pedigree human as much prone to recessive gene problems as the pedigree dogs that we saw in an earlier chapter (see page 30). So, having fought to eliminate one set of inherited conditions, we might end up with a stack more.

Reprogramming germ cells (producing sperm or eggs) is very controversial. The Clothier Committee, set up by the Department of Health in the UK, has recommended a temporary halt on all such experiments, and says that gene therapy should only be used to alleviate genetic disease, but not to change normal human characteristics.[387] But will the recommendations be obeyed? Screening for genetic defects is also a 'ferocious minefield' which raises problems of confidentiality, insurance and employment.[388]

In Denmark, a textile mill recently allowed 226 of its workers to be screened for deficiency of a particular enzyme called alpha-1 antitrypsin. People without it are very vulnerable to lung irritation and infection of the lungs. Although the information was collected for research only, trade union officials pointed out that the information could have been used as a basis on which to fire workers, and factories might in future only employ disease-resistant workers instead of improving working conditions.[389]

The Danish Parliament has recently debated the use of genetic information by insurance companies, and Baroness Warnock has called on the UK government to ban insurance companies from asking for genetic screening.[390] The key questions are these: Who owns my genetic information, and who has the right to know what is written in my genes?[391]

Computer dating by gene matching

It has already been seriously suggested that in the future some people may choose their marriage partners on the basis of their genetic code—on their spit, to be precise, since a sample of saliva contains enough cells to analyse genetic makeup. A journalist from *The Independent* took the test out of interest, remarking that statistically 16,000 who read the paper that day were carrying a defective cystic fibrosis gene, including an estimated twenty-three of the paper's own staff.

By March 1992 almost 3,000 people in Watford and South East Hertfordshire had already been screened through the spitting test, as part of a survey to see if it is worth screening all adults in the country.[392] There are now three large-scale surveys of healthy individuals going on in London, Cardiff and Edinburgh to see how many carry the cystic fibrosis gene. In future the spit test could be used to reveal if someone has a genetic susceptibility to Alzheimer's disease, heart disease or some cancers. In fact pre-engagement screening is nothing new. For some time many Jewish people have been screened at their own request for Tay-Sachs disease.

The problem is that information can bring a terrible burden, as well as a need for expert in-depth counselling based on a detailed understanding of some of these illnesses. As a recently published report said:

> For many of these disorders, the ability to predict the risk of disease will antedate preventive and therapeutic interventions by many years. During this lag phase, issues concerning the validity of the tests, the severity of the diseases for which screening is offered, the safety of the interventions, and the autonomy of the pregnant woman in deciding to be screened are important.[393]

Living in the real world

You may feel that all abortion is wrong, whatever the circumstances, and that in the words of the new Danish law passed in 1988 establishing an ethical council 'human life takes as its beginning the time of conception'.[394] Such a rule may be simple and clear, but for those who have to work through the consequences in terms of individual tragedy, life can be far less cut and dried—even for those who regard the Bible as their source of ultimate authority.

Two different mothers my wife and I know well gave birth

over the last four years, knowing that the baby being born had a heart defect so severe that the baby was unlikely to live for more than a few days after birth. In both cases the parents were informed of the problem during pregnancy following routine ultrasound examinations, repeated a few weeks later. Both couples were offered abortions, which they were very unhappy about—especially as by the time the baby had grown large enough for the ultrasound to be accurate it was getting quite late in the pregnancy.

Both families felt their babies were already alive, and were already or about to be conscious. They felt their babies were comfortable, moving around contented and secure inside the womb, and had an existence of their own. In both instances the birth itself was relatively straightforward, and mother and baby were quickly home. Some two to four days later each baby became weaker, and died quite quickly and peacefully.

Personal tragedy

Another friend of mine came up to me recently to tell me some sad news. I knew his wife was expecting another baby and I had been delighted for them both. He is an evangelical church leader and has supported the pro-life anti-abortion campaign. With tears in his eyes he described how doctors had seen a major problem on the scan—a very severe malformation affecting the head and brain. It seemed there was no chance at all of the child living after birth. Faced with the situation after much consideration, thought and prayer both he and his wife felt it right to have an abortion. When the baby was delivered at around twenty weeks, gross abnormalities were obvious: most of the head was missing, confirming the diagnosis of anencephaly. My purpose is not to comment on whether they were right or wrong, but to make us think.

Taking a risk

These are very difficult and distressing areas. In many ways life was much simpler before pre-natal screening. What about the couple who have an inheritable disease, which is so serious that they will not consider having any children at all unless some guarantee is there that the child will not be affected? Two friends of ours were married some years ago. Among many other things they have in common, they share this problem: both of them walk with a limp because of a congenital malformation of the hip joint, so that one hip is permanently dislocated. For them both it was incorrectly diagnosed and treated when they were children. This condition can be inherited.

Their first child had the same condition, and had to spend several weeks in hospital on more than one occasion to help correct the problem. Perhaps our friends would welcome some way of ensuring that their next child has normal hips, although at least here the condition is not life-threatening and is treatable. Unfortunately, gene experts are a long way from being able to test sperm or eggs genetically before conception, so the only option likely to be available for the near future is an embryo test accompanied by the offer of an abortion. Looking further ahead, there may be the prospect of embryo reprogramming.[395]

However, such action could introduce a new mutation and a new disease or condition. The risks may be unacceptable to correct a defect for someone as yet unborn, rather than in someone who is already born and very ill. The simpler and more predictable alternative is always likely to be testing of foetuses and selective abortions.[396]

Problems of infertility

Infertility is a particularly common problem these days for two reasons: the first is that many people are delaying getting married or thinking about starting to have a family. Fertility drops quite steeply from the age of around twenty-eight onwards, so many couples who would have had slight difficulties conceiving a child in their early twenties are now faced with a much greater problem. The other reason is related to the steadily rising numbers of cases of sexually transmitted diseases each year—over 580,000 new cases in the UK alone in 1991.

One complication can be Pelvic Inflammatory Disease, which is often caused by a tiny organism called chlamydia. This can be very hard indeed to get rid of. Over a period of years, chronic infection leads to fibrous thickening in the pelvis, which damages the delicate fallopian tubes used to carry the egg from the ovary to the uterus. In some cases the eggs can no longer travel down, nor can sperm travel up. In other cases, eggs become stuck as they are gently propelled along the tiny tube. Sperm still swim up the other way with the result that an egg becomes fertilised in the tube, where it remains as it divides. The developing ball of cells implants in the tube instead of in the womb.

The tube has no thick muscular lining to implant into and there are no suitable blood vessels to feed the developing placenta. The pregnancy that results is highly dangerous and is a common cause of a medical emergency in women, with acute pain and massive internal bleeding caused by the burrowing of the embryo through the tube wall and bleeding from large blood vessels.

Children for families

With increasing infertility, and a low threshold for abortion, there are very few babies available for adoption these days—certainly nothing like enough to meet the hopes of over five infertile couples in every hundred. Therefore the pressure is on to use every available method to provide children for people. It is a sad irony that many who don't want babies are conceiving and aborting them, while many others desperate to be pregnant continue to be childless.

Strong arguments can be made in favour of correcting gene defects in parents to enhance their ability to have their own healthy children. This is as an alternative to embryo or foetus testing and abortion. Strong arguments can also be made in favour of reprogramming an embryo, so long as gene changes are absolutely necessary to avoid, say, death in early adult life, and the procedure is known to be safe. A most important distinction here is between a genetic repair, almost like micro-surgery on a chromosome, and a genetic adaptation introducing genes that would never have been part of the code of those parents, to improve physique or intelligence for example.

However, because such reprogramming introduces new genes which could be transmitted to subsequent generations with unknown results, and safety would be impossible to determine ethically, I am opposed to germ line or embryo modification in humans. Changing somatic cells in foetuses during pregnancy might be acceptable, in the same way as gene therapy for somatic cells in children or adults. These changes would allow a defective part of the body to function normally without altering the genes of sperm or eggs of the person treated. It would involve injecting modified cells into the organs of a foetus in the womb.

Foetal transplants

I am also very unhappy about transplanting human foetal tissue into people, because such tissues are obtained from induced abortions. Tissues transplanted from a stillborn child, or from a miscarriage, are a different matter, similar to the use of transplanted organs obtained from adults who have died. It seems there are pressures enough on people these days to have abortions and the odds are becoming more and more stacked against the survival of the foetus.

Current regulations state that there must not be any relationship between an abortion clinic and those doing research. This is to try and avoid abuses that could arise in times of pressure to complete research or to treat patients. I do not feel happy about any kind of experimentation on embryos, although some could say straight away that without it, we may never make any progress in areas I have said earlier could be ethically acceptable to use as proven treatments. A recent Gallup Poll showed that more people are opposed to embryo research than are in favour of it (51% to 38%).[397]

Early experiments

I am slightly less uneasy about experiments on fertilised eggs or on small balls of cells up to the first week or so of life. Part of this is the need to be consistent. If we are really going to take the moment of conception as our starting point for the protection of human life, then we should do away with the coil as a method of contraception, for a start. The reason for saying this is that the coil does not prevent fertilisation of an egg by sperm. It works by preventing the developing ball of cells from implanting in the womb some five to seven days after conception. In the strictest sense, a coil produces a possible abortion every month.

I do not believe it is right to fertilise human eggs deliberately for the purpose of experiments. This seems to me to trivialise the nature of life itself. Nor do I think it is ethical to fertilise more eggs than are likely to be needed for implantation into the mother's womb. It is the latter practice which has produced thousands of surplus embryos each year—embryos which can either be washed down the sink or grown for a while in the test-tube.

The main reason given for fertilising so many eggs at once is that unfertilised eggs cannot be stored. Without a store of eggs in the laboratory, the mother may need to have another minor operation to obtain some more if she wants to have another baby.

These are all very difficult questions which become harder to answer as you examine each problem more closely.

Humanised germs

I cannot see any ethical objection to using a bit of human genetic code to tell a bacterium what you want it to do. Nor can I see any real difficulty in enhancing the genetic code of plants or animals. It would seem to be a logical outworking of the ancient command given to man by God, recorded in Genesis, to be fruitful and subdue the earth.[398] God has given it to us to enjoy and be its custodians. Why shouldn't we make bacteria and viruses work for us? After all, they give us enough problems and misery with the diseases they so often cause.

However, I would draw the line at attempts to give another mammal significant parts of the human genetic code. As we have seen, the Bible teaches us that when God made us, he made us in his own image.[399] We are not the same as monkeys or baboons, and therefore efforts to blur the distinctions genetically would seem to be wrong. Even laying aside religious or philosophical issues, it is obvious that such experiments could have massive social and psychological implications for the new beings and for the rest of society.

Is it right to patent life?

The ethics of patenting new life forms is an important and difficult area which we have looked at in detail earlier (pages

62–64). We could start from the position that since all creation belongs to God the Creator, it is not right to seek to patent a life form. Most patents (99%) are taken out by industrialised nations, so developing nations are hardly likely to benefit. Patents on life are likely to lead to large payments from poor countries to multinational companies for the right to continue effective farming.

However, it could be argued that without patent protection, companies will not bother to invest, and new advances such as insulin production by bacteria will not be made. One answer to the patent question would be to fund gene research entirely from public money and to regard inventions and discoveries as public property. However, this is likely to be very inefficient. A compromise might be to allow patents on single cell modifications, such as new bacteria or monoclonal antibodies, but to refuse patents on multi-cellular organisms, including animals.

Animal welfare is important

Many gene experiments are so risky for the creature concerned that they would never be permitted on humans. Many approaches are designed to increase meat or milk yield, making each animal body work more intensively than by natural design. Already we have seen overstimulated cows with severe mastitis (page 86), and giving birth to giants (page 92).

We are also seeing pigs develop with severe arthritis, partial blindness and impotence. Other experiments have created animals designed to suffer. The oncomouse, for example, always develops cancer in ninety days. The entire existence of the species is based on the need to find a cancer cure, but the approach may be disturbing to some. As custodians of God's creation we have to ask ourselves whether we are behaving in a way which pleases him.

The issues of right and wrong are complex yet vitally important. They make us think about the definition of humanity itself and about the ultimate purpose of creation. There are profound social, emotional, physical and spiritual implications which need urgent consideration. Meanwhile, our knowledge grows daily and gives us ever greater power over life. The Christian view is that life is a wonderful gift from God, and human beings are his design, in his own image. We have been given the ability to learn about and control our world, but not the authority to destroy it or to alter our own nature fundamentally. Our guiding principles should be respect and love for others and for our world, and a commitment, for the best results, to follow our Maker's instructions. However, even those with no religious convictions at all are likely to want to reject some of the possibilities raised in earlier chapters.

11

A Ten-Point Gene Charter

If you have read through this far (or just skipped to the end), you may be hoping for a grand finale to this massive explosion of new science: a way forward drawing together all the potential, with some neat and tidy solutions to the problems and risks.

We have already seen that government controls will be hard to draw up and hard to enforce—even if we can agree on what they should be. We have also seen how easy it will be to avoid controls unless they are backed by international agreement. Finally, we have seen that the gene revolution raises so many commercial, philosophical and spiritual issues that international agreement will be very hard to obtain.

Without delay the government should introduce a Gene Charter: ten vitally needed measures backed by law, designed to protect human safety, to safeguard the environment and to provide ethical standards.

Here is a proposed starting point for consumers, theologians, commercial and political leaders to discuss. While we could argue for ever about exact wording, the technology marches on. There should therefore be a great sense of urgency to adopt a clear charter, not just in the UK and EC, but across the industrialised world, aiming eventually to include every nation in an international agreement. Some parts of the proposed charter are already covered to a greater or lesser degree by existing or proposed UK legislation.

A GENE CHARTER

1. Testing of new foods

The government should set up a formal specialist licensing authority, backed by law, to approve for human consumption all foods that contain the products of genetic modification. The decision-making body must have good representation from consumer groups as well as food scientists. Licences should be required to cover not only where germ cells have been reprogrammed, but also where the organism contains a subgroup of altered cells. All voluntary reporting systems should be made compulsory, with failure to comply a criminal offence.

Particular attention needs to be paid to the possibility of introducing substances into the human diet on a large scale which could turn out to have cancer-inducing, foetus-damaging or other toxic effects.

All genetically engineered foods or food additives should be subject to rigorous chemical analysis and testing to determine what new or unfamiliar compounds may now be contained in the food. The amount of analysis needed will depend on the degree of reprogramming.

2. Food labelling requirements

It should be made illegal to sell or attempt to sell to the public any food containing products of gene technology without clear labelling so that consumers can choose. Even where experts have passed the food as safe, many consumers may have personal reservations about the ethics or safety of some of the techniques used to produce the food and should be entitled to clear unambiguous information.

3. Environmental release of new organisms

It should be made illegal to release into the environment any genetically modified organisms without a licence, regardless of whether there has been proven damage to people, property or the environment. There should be heavy fines for accidental release without having to prove damage or negligence.

In some countries such as the UK, some controls have been in existence for some time, albeit as part of a voluntary code of practice.[400] These controls should apply especially to micro-organisms, plants, fish, birds and animals which could survive if they escaped from a contained area on a farm. Controls do not need to be so strict with conventional farm livestock, although such stock should be indelibly marked in such a way as to make their origin and nature instantly recognisable. Breeding of fish in a confined pond with no water outlet from it might be a borderline area, but should also require a licence.

4. Viral contamination controls

Viral spread outside the laboratory as a result of genetic research is a serious possibility—whether spread of plasmids, of plant viruses, of animal viruses, or of viruses infecting humans. In the absence of effective anti-viral cures, we have to recognise the great vulnerability humans have to plague, or another pandemic like AIDS, but this time maybe of an even worse nature, spread, say, by respiratory droplets rather than by sexual intercourse or through the blood, and killing people in weeks or months rather than years.

We need to acknowledge that many countries of the world do now have all the resources to make by laboratory accident even more dangerous viruses than HIV. It should be recognised that there is already evidence that genetically engineered viruses given to animals have the potential to mix uncontrollably with other viruses already present, with unpredictable and possibly disastrous effects.[401]

All procedures involving the reprogramming or reassembling of viruses should be strictly controlled, with permits required by law in advance rather than reporting after the event. In particular, there should be a special licensing authority for experiments where animals or plants are being infected by synthetic viruses. Fewer controls are needed for test-tube infections of cell lines in culture, except where infected cells are replaced in plants or animals.

5. Ban on biological warfare research

There should be an immediate cessation of research into new biological weapons of any kind. Urgent international agreement should be sought through the United Nations to close biological weapons factories, destroy stockpiles and cease research.

This will be very difficult to enforce because germ weapons production can be hidden inside any chemical factory. There should be reciprocal arrangements between nations to allow free observer access, helping to enforce the ban.

6. Control of human cell modification

There should be an immediate permanent formal ban on attempts to reprogram human germ line cells. Failure to do this will open the door by definition to a number of new types, variants or mutants of human beings, with unthinkable consequences ethically and socially. Gene modifications designed to alter normal human characteristics, for example height or intelligence, could have devastating consequences for the human race. A temporary ban on human germ line modification has been recommended by the Clothier committee set up by the Department of Health, but had not been implemented by early 1993.[402]

7. Limits on genetic screening

(a) Pre-birth screening
It should become a criminal offence to attempt to analyse the products of conception from fertilised egg to foetus in order to be able selectively to destroy those without desired genetic

characteristics within the normal range. This would prevent, for example, clinics advertising services designed to increase the chances of having a baby with ultra-high intelligence.

Attempts to prevent babies of the 'wrong' sex from being conceived should cease, except where there is a strong possibility of serious sex-linked disease. The detection of foetuses with genes predisposing to disease is a sensitive and controversial issue, which is dominated by the outcome of the debate in each country over the ethics of abortion.

Every effort should be directed towards gene therapies that will allow effective post-natal correction of serious gene defects, thus moving resources from mass destruction of life to cure.

(b) Genetic screening of adults and children

Genetic screening of adults or children should only be carried out at the specific request of the person to be screened, or at the request of parents, and only where the result is likely to be of direct benefit to the individual or other members of his or her family. Screening for jobs, insurance or any other reason should cease, unless in the direct interests of the health of the individual and at that person's request.

(c) Human cloning

There should be a ban on cloning where the result may be to produce a human being with genetic guarantees and zero genetic variation.

(d) Gene therapy

Where gene therapy is used medically to alter somatic cells, long-term monitoring of possible effects on offspring should be overseen by a regulatory authority independent of those responsible for the original research.[403] Such treatments should only be offered to those with serious genetic disease. This is to prevent a slide towards treating the trivial as a front for modifying normal human traits not associated with disease.[404]

8. Restrictions on altering animals

(a) Animal germ line modifications
Germ line modifications in animals should be subject to formal licensing, with a ban on adding human DNA to animal genomes unless it is strictly limited to the DNA fragment needed to produce a human substance, such as a hormone or Factor 8. For example, it would then become illegal to attempt to insert large chunks of human DNA into developing monkey embryos.

(b) Welfare of new animals
Every effort should be made to ensure that new breeds or species are healthy by constitution, and not prone to extra risks of illness, discomfort or disability as a result of human interference.

Where additional health problems are noted in a new variant, every effort should be made to prevent further breeding from such stock so the suffering variant is not perpetuated. The only exception permitted should be the oncomouse already in existence, if bred under carefully regulated conditions, with a high regard for animal welfare, and for the sole purpose of finding a cure for cancer.

9. Public access to and ownership of information

There has never been an area of science with such far-reaching implications for the future of life on earth. The world impact of a genetic experiment which goes badly wrong could be greater than any other single man-made disaster—greater even than the exploding of several nuclear bombs. Nuclear fallout is mainly confined to one area or continent, unlike an out-of-control infectious disease agent which could devastate the population of every country.

The public should have full and free access to public registers of genetic modifications in progress and licences applied for. There should be full public representation at all important committees, and hearings should be open to observers by arrangement.

Genetically modified animals, plants or other organisms licensed for release under (3) above should be able to be cultivated or bred without patent restrictions in exactly the same way as any other breeds developed by conventional means in the past, with the exception of single-cell organisms such as bacteria-producing medicines, or human cell lines in culture-producing human hormones.

For single-cell organisms and cell lines, new 'inventions' and new techniques used to produce gene changes should be eligible for protection under patent for no more than twenty years from the date of creation.

Patents should not be allowed for unaltered sections of the human genome.

10. Submission of gene activity to ethical review

Gene modification raises vitally important ethical issues which should influence licensing arrangements so that decisions are not merely made on practical or safety considerations. These issues relate to animal welfare as well as human. They also relate to the ethics of patenting new life forms, including animals, and to the possible negative impact of high-tech gene changes on agriculture in developing countries.

There should be wide public representation on ethics committees, including representatives from Christian and other religious groups. The decisions of the committee should take into account the following principles:

(a) Safeguarding the future of our world

Our world is a limited fragile resource that must be protected from human actions likely to affect future generations.

(b) Uniqueness of human life

Human life is the highest life form in the known universe, and those of Christian and many other faiths regard it as a sacred mystery.

It is essential that world agreement is reached on a basic gene charter as soon as possible, to cover some if not all of the above.

At the moment it is too easy for those wishing to avoid any controls to move the base of their operations from one country to another. Controls then damage the economy of the country enforcing them. There also needs to be a global consistency in the way regulations are interpreted and applied from country to country.

A world summit on biotechnology is urgently needed, perhaps organised by the World Health Organisation as part of United Nations.

ACTION PLAN FOR CONSUMERS

What can you or I do that will make a difference to how gene technology is being used? Here is a four-point plan.

1. Talk about it

Most people you know have little or no idea about what is going on already and what is just around the corner. Talk to your friends about some of the things in this book, or let them see a copy. Whenever you hear issues of conservation, two-thirds world or consumerism mentioned, make sure people understand how the gene revolution is going to affect us all.

2. Write about it

When you see or hear in the media new reports about gene modifications, write to your MP and Euro MP expressing any concerns you may have. For many it may be only the first or second letter they will ever have received on the subject. This is a very new area, so they will appreciate your information. Issues relating to food labelling and public information can be raised now, together with other parts of the Gene Charter. There may be other opportunities where you can express a view in writing, or otherwise inform people.

3. Pray about it

If like me you share a strong Christian faith, then you will appreciate the power and importance of prayer. You can pray in the area of genetic engineering, 'Your kingdom come, your will be done on earth as it is in heaven.'[405] Pray for sensitivity and respect for God's creation, especially for human life, and for all those grappling with complex, agonising decisions regarding medical treatments and research. Pray that through understanding more of the science of life, people will be prompted to consider its ultimate meaning and will discover its purpose.

4. Join with others

You may wish to join an association that has a concern about these issues and is seeking to be a helpful and responsible influence. Several are listed in the names and addresses in Appendix 3.

In conclusion, the gene revolution is the most powerful scientific revolution in the history of human discovery, with the power to change every aspect of our lives, and even to change irreversibly the nature of human life itself. The revolution promises us spectacular benefits, but brings frightening new problems, and poses heart-rending ethical and spiritual dilemmas. The revolution has already begun and accelerates every day, yet few have even the faintest glimmer of awareness of what is happening. How are you going to respond to the challenge we face?

The days are over when we could just sit back and let science run its course. If we do not take control of advancing gene technology now, then it will take control of us by changing the very roots of our society and of our being. The facts about the gene revolution need to be clearly understood so there can be an urgent public debate, followed by effective international regulation. Only then can the quality of life on earth be improved without threatening the future of the human race.

APPENDIX I

Christian Medical Fellowship Submission to British Medical Association on Genetic Engineering

(Extract from the *Journal of the Christian Medical Fellowship* [January 1990], pp 18–22 and reproduced by kind permission with some abbreviations. Please note that enormous strides forward have been made in what is possible since the submission was drafted. It should also be borne in mind that it has been written largely by clinical geneticists and therefore has a particular perspective.)

Submission to the BMA working party on genetic engineering from the specialist committee on Genetics of the Christian Medical Fellowship (CMF) . . . a membership of around 4,500 British doctors.

The nature of humanity

A major concern of the public about 'genetic engineering' relates to manipulation of the embryo and the prospect of the creation of human beings who have been designed either for perfection or for specific tasks. Although such creations are not remotely possible for technical reasons, there are other factors of over-riding importance.

Christians believe human beings to be made in the image of God and uniquely different from other species. They therefore have great potential for acting wisely and caringly towards their fellows and their environment in harmony and obedience to their Creator.

Although genetic manipulation may have the capacity to reduce the incidence of disease, and perhaps even to influence certain personality traits, such manipulation can never alter man's intrinsic responsibility for his behaviour towards his Creator.

Those with 'favourable' genetic endowments have to make choices between good and evil in the same way as those who have a poor genetic makeup. Privilege brings responsibility but does not confer automatic morality. No amount of favourable genetic manipulation can improve morality or delete self-centredness.

General considerations

The CMF emphasises the importance of justice, truth, equity, and man's role as steward of God's creation. We would stress the importance of:

1. The *Essential Value* of the individual.

2. *Education*—that people are accurately informed about what is possible in this field and the potential hazards. Efforts should be made to redress some of the more sensational reports by the media. This will become particularly important as mass screening of healthy individuals becomes possible. The impact of such screening programmes on the individuals concerned is of paramount importance, and freedom of choice must be safeguarded.

3. *Environment*—apart from emphasis on man's responsibility as steward, we have no particular contribution to issues involving agriculture and animal husbandry but welcome the contribution that genetic manipulation can make towards the relief of hunger and poverty.

4. *Exploitation*—Christians are concerned that the individual, particularly if weak or disadvantaged in any way, is protected. Those who might be benefited by advances in genetic research are vulnerable to being persuaded to be 'guinea pigs' and exploited either commercially or by prestige-seeking research workers.

The child needs protection and the status of the embryo and foetus must also be considered. Counselling should be provided by well-informed sympathetic clinicians, particularly clinical geneticists rather than by those whose commitment is primarily to research. Problems of commercialisation and patenting of 'probes' and genetically engineered products such as Factor 8 need to be considered and this is discussed further below.

5. *Expense*—the Human Genome Project is very expensive and may divert funds from other causes. Whether this project should be undertaken in toto, or whether the search should focus on disease-related sequences, is a contentious issue. Where funds are limited we would favour a search for disease-related sequences rather than an attempt to unravel the entire genome.

Once established, the use of molecular methods for the treatment and prevention of genetically determined disorders should not be unacceptably expensive, particularly when compared with current managements of these at present largely intractable diseases.

Specific considerations

Genetic engineering can be considered from two aspects: either the alteration of the genetic makeup of a somatic cell or the alteration of the genetic makeup of a zygote in vitro prior to implantation. The former, though not yet practicable, may well become so. The latter is a very remote possibility, partly because of technical difficulty, but chiefly because it is unlikely to be chosen by any parental couple who have the alternate option of choosing implantation of an embryo shown to be free from the genetic defect for which they are at risk. We have therefore included here a discussion on the choice of a particular embryo.

1. The use of somatic cells

Although not yet established it could become technically possible to use somatic cells which have been genetically altered for the treatment of single gene disorders such as haemoglobinopathies. The patient's malfunctioning precursor cells would be replaced or supplemented by cells with normal gene function.

Development of such replacement therapy is ethically little different from the development of any other potentially hazardous novel form of treatment, except in one significant respect: the use of living cells is involved.

Our ignorance of the control of gene expression introduces a new element with regard to the safety of such techniques. Although the ethical issues are generally very similar to those involved in organ transplantation, there is an additional factor in that stem cell multiplication for the rest of the patient's life is an integral part of the procedure. If the treatment of a child with a haemoglobinopathy were successful, the 'new' cell line would be expected to function for decades in a controlled and normal manner.

2. The pre-implantation embryo

Members of the CMF vary in their views as to the status of the fertilised ovum and pre-implantation embryo. Many believe that from the time of fertilisation the 'image of God' is present, thus making the embryo a unique person who should be recognised and treated in all respects as a neighbour. They would therefore find all the following techniques unacceptable.

Others believe that although at these early stages the pre-implantation embryo is indisputably human, it has not yet the attributes of the 'image of God' and so may be manipulated or discarded.

Nevertheless, there must be a time at which such attributes and status are attained. All members agree that once they are attained, that individual is of infinite value. All agree too that the relationships between husband and wife, parent and child are of central importance both for the well-being of the individual and for the whole of society. We believe that children are entrusted to their parents to be nurtured and brought to maturity as individuals in their own right.

When parents start to see their children as items whose desirability depends on their quality, then the loving acceptance of the child simply by virtue of who he or she is could be lost.

All parents desire the best for their child and that he or she will be free of defect, but we must guard against the development of consumerist attitudes. Perfection is unlikely to be attainable and some couples have unrealistic expectations. The child should not be brought into the world to gratify parental aspirations.

(i) Pre-implantation gene detection

(a) Pathological genes: at present, observation and manipulation of the pre-implantation embryo are chiefly research orientated, though with the aim of clinical application. However, it is now becoming possible to detect the presence or absence of a single gene in a single cell taken from a developing blastocyst and this would allow the development of pre-implantation pre-natal diagnosis. This is already being questioned by those who find even first trimester termination of pregnancy unacceptable or highly distressing.

The unacceptability of the necessary research procedures is a major contra-indication for some CMF members as mentioned earlier. Apart from this the chief ethical problems are those of the safety of the technique to the developing embryo and the expense and low success rates of pregnancy necessarily dependent on these in-vitro techniques.

(b) Sex ascertainment: the sex of the blastocyst would probably be discovered from the initial testing. If so, it would be possible for the parents' preference to be the arbiter of which healthy blastocysts should be implanted, if the opportunity presents itself. The pragmatic see no ethical objection to this while others believe that random choice should be maintained as in the natural lottery.

However, use of these techniques simply to achieve a child of the desired sex would be unacceptable to all, as a matter of inappropriate use of scarce resources is an additional factor.

(c) The detection of non-pathological single gene traits: as technology expands, the number of detectable traits can be expected to expand. Some identifiable genes will give rise to minor abnormalities (eg missing incisor teeth) and others to traits which in themselves are harmless, but which indicate increased risk of pathology in later life (eg hypercholesterolemia). Yet others will code for normal variants such as eye or hair colour. How this information is used is by no means straightforward and the comments made on consumerism are particularly helpful here.

There will be a need for regular discussion and review. In (a), (b) and (c) above the pre-implantation embryos have all been the genetic offspring of the parents so that any gene detected in the pre-implantation embryo would already be present in one or other parent. There is no introduction of novel genes into the 'family', but simply decisions as to which familial contributions would appear in the offspring.

(ii) Embryo donation

The ethics of gamete and embryo donation will not be discussed further here. Their use is acceptable to some CMF members but not to others. Pre-implantation gene detection however could enable recipient couples to choose donated embryos with certain genes known to be present or absent. This is not possible at present, though it is inherently possible at present for those using artificial insemination by donor (AID), and ethical guidelines should be similar to those recommended for AID or ovum donation, though again constant review is essential.

(iii) Gene 'correction' and alteration techniques applied to the embryo

This is still a hypothetical situation which is fraught with ethical difficulty and highly contentious. It will not be discussed further here . . . the fact that any gene changes are then fixed permanently in the germ cells of the offspring makes this an area which should probably remain unexplored at present. The possibility of unforeseeable effects arising in a future generation is a strong deterrent, besides the fact that there are sufficient unknown factors to contend with among the topics already discussed.

(iv) Any form of commercial transaction is unacceptable.

(v) Any form of 'trait selection' by government or other agencies is unacceptable.

3. Other techniques

(i) Twinning, ie making multiple identical copies from a single blastocyst with the object of producing a sibship of identical children.

(ii) Cloning, ie insertion of nucleus from a donor's somatic cell into an enucleated ovum in order to make a carbon copy of the donor.

(iii) Chimerism, ie fusion of human and animal gametes to proceed to blastocyst or beyond.

All these are unacceptable since we believe that humans, made in the image of God, are distinct from the animals and should remain so. Each individual is unique and that distinctiveness is important both to that person and to society. It is true that identical twins occur naturally and that each is a person in his or her own right, but some twins do have difficulties establishing their own identity.

4. The availability of gene products

As sequencing of the human genome proceeds it is likely that an increasing number of gene products will become manufacturable. Factor 8, insulin and growth hormone are already available. . . . Like other substances, growth hormone is being used illegally by athletes and at the same time paediatricians are having to decide whether it should be administered to physiologically short children.

Patenting and marketing of products produced by these techniques for therapeutic use should be subject to the same clinical restraints as operate for medications produced by other means. The difficulty arises when products can alter physiological traits. As more become available the ethical implications of each will have to be reviewed, with particular regard to commercial exploitation and the desirability of their use in altering physiological rather than pathological traits.

Experience with growth hormone shows that there can be considerable parental pressure to use the product. Meticulous studies on safety, and honest discussion of risks and benefits, will be essential. As new substances are produced, their use should be strictly controlled and proper clinical trials conducted over several years with even greater stringency than that applied to new medicines.

This is probably the most immediate area needing firm ethical guidelines since this technology is imminently available.

Conclusions

Recombinant DNA techniques have enormous scope for revolutionising both biology and medicine. Manipulation of genetic material has far-reaching consequences for both this and subsequent generations. The Christian Medical Fellowship believes that we as doctors should act as stewards, helping mankind to make the most of its potential and prepared to correct abnormalities, but not as dictators, manipulating all for selfish ends.

Inevitably there is a difference of opinion as to where these roles begin and end. Some feel that work on early embryos is unacceptably interfering and that the risk of disaster outweighs the potential benefits. Others believe that cautious exploration is the right way forward. All Christian Medical Fellowship members agree that we are responsible now to our patients and their families, but ultimately responsible to our Creator for the decisions we make today.

References

1. Report of the committee of enquiry into human fertilisation and embryology (HMSO, 1984).

Members of the CMF specialist standing committee on genetics are:
    Dr C. Berry, Consultant Clinical Geneticist, Guy's Hospital London
    Dr S. Bundey, Senior Lecturer in Clinical Genetics, Infant Development Unit, Birmingham University
    Dr A. Johnston, Consultant Physician, Aberdeen Royal Infirmary

Appendix 2
Further Reading

'CM 1788 Report of the Committee on the Ethics of Gene Therapy White Paper Sir Cyril Clothier' (HMSO), £6.90.

'Guidelines on the assessment of novel foods and processes.' Published by Dept Health no 38 Report on Health and Social Subjects. HMSO, PO Box 276, London SW8 5DT. Tel 071–873–9090. £4.25.

'Heredity: Science and Society: on the possibilities and limits of Genetic testing and gene therapy' (Committee of the Health Council of The Netherlands: The Hague, Dfl 165, 1989) 196 pages.

'Health and Safety Executive: A Guide to the HSW Act' (HSW Booklet HS(R)6, 2nd edition, HMSO: London, 1983, Royal College of Physicians).

'Genetic engineering: Christian responsibilities in today's world', papers from conference in October 1992 organised by Christians in Science and the Christian Medical Fellowship. Full set £5 from Christian Medical Fellowship—see address in Appendix 3.

N. Cameron, *The New Medicine* (Hodder & Stoughton, 1991).

A.C. Berry, *The Rites of Life* (Hodder & Stoughton, 1987).

D. Weaver, *Catalog of Prenatally Diagnosed Conditions* (Johns Hopkins, 1992).

V. McKusick, *Mendelian Inheritance in Man* (Johns Hopkins, 1992).

A. Milunsky, *Genetic Disorders and the Fetus* (Johns Hopkins, 1992).

N. Ford, *When did I begin? Conception of the human individual in history, philosophy and science* (Cambridge University Press, 1988).

Houghton & Houghton, *Coping with Childlessness* (Allen and Unwin, 1984).

D.G. Jones, *Manufacturing humans. The challenge of the new reproductive technologies* (IVP, 1987).

D.R.J. Macer, *Shaping Genes* (Eubios, 1990).

N. Cameron, *Embryos and Ethics, the Warnock report in debate* (Rutherford House: Edinburgh, 1987).

D.G. Jones, *Brave New People: Ethical issues at the commencement of life* (IVP, 1984).

J. Stott, *Issues Facing Christians Today* (IVP, 1991).

P. Dixon, *The Truth About AIDS* (Kingsway, 1990).

R. Higginson, *Whose baby? The ethics of in vitro fertilisation* (Marshall Pickering, 1988).

R. Winter, *Choose Life* (Marshall Pickering, 1988).

G. Nossal & R. Coppel, *Reshaping Life* (Cambridge, 1989).

Genetic Engineering: your responsibilities under the regulations (IND(G) 86 L. Available from the Health and Safety Executive).

T. Lang, *Food Fit for the World?* (SAFE Publications: 21 Tower St, London WC2H 9NS, 1992), £7.50.

B.P. Ager, 'Oversight of Genetic Manipulation in the UK', *Journal of Health and Safety* (27–31 July 1988), p 1.

'Report of the Committee of Inquiry into Human Fertilisation and Embryology' (Warnock Report) (Department of Health HMSO, 1984).

D.J. Weatherall, *The New Genetics and Clinical Practice*, 3rd Edition (Oxford University Press, 1991).

J.M. Connor, *Essential Medical Genetics*, 3rd Edition (Blackwell Scientific Publications, 1991).

Patent concern: patenting of plants and animals (Genetic Forum).

Bishop and Waldholz, *Genome* (Simon and Schuster: New York, 1990).

APPENDIX 3
Useful Addresses

Inclusion should not be taken to indicate endorsement of agency activity or materials.

Advisory Committee on Genetic Manipulation
Health and Safety Executive
Room 532
Baynards House
Chepstow Place
London W2 4TF
Tel: 071–243 6120

Advisory Committee on Novel Food Processes
Ministry of Agriculture, Fisheries and Food
Ergon House
c/o Nobel House
17 Smith Square
London SW1P 3JR
Tel: 071–238 6167

Agricultural and Food Research Council
Public Relations
Wiltshire Court
Farnsby Street
Swindon SN1 5AT
Tel: 0793 514242

Biotechnology Unit
Laboratory of the Government Chemist
Queens Road
Teddington
Middlesex TW11 OLY
Tel: 081–943 7381

British Medical Association
(Working Party on Genetic Engineering)
BMA House
Tavistock Square
London WC1H 9JP
Tel: 071–387 4499

British Technology Group
Science Division
101 Newington Causeway
London SE1 6BU
Tel: 071–403 6666

*BTG invested £10 million in 1989/90 for genetic engineering
projects with commercial application.*

CARE
Christian Policy Analyst: medical ethics and life issues
53 Romney Street
London SW1P 3RF
Tel: 071–233 0455

Christian Medical Fellowship
Specialist Standing Committee on Genetics
157 Waterloo Road
London SE1 8XN
Tel: 071–928 4694

Christians in Science
66 Silverknowes Parkway
Edinburgh EH4 5LA
Tel: 031–336 1173

Committee on Ethics of Gene Therapy
Department of Health
Room 418 Wellington House
153–155 Waterloo Road
London SE1 8UG
Tel: 071–972 4193

Committee continuing informal monitoring while public consultation continues on the Clothier Report (qv). 'If proposal for gene therapy made to local ethic committee then copy also to the committee. Consultation to be completed on 18 May 1992. A substantive mechanism is then likely to be set up—independently of government.'

Consumer Safety Unit
Department of Trade and Industry
Room 416
10–18 Victoria Street
London SW1H ONN
Tel: 071–215 3272

Environmental release/sewage disposal
Department of Environment
Romney House
43 Marsham Street
London SW1P 3PY

Evangelical Alliance
Information Officer
Whitefield House
186 Kennington Park Road
London SE11 4BT
Tel: 071–582 0228

Food Labelling
Food Standards Division
Ministry of Agriculture, Food and Fisheries
Branch A
Room 312
Ergon House

c/o Nobel House
17 Smith Square
London SW1P 3HX
Tel: 071–238 6281

Also Novel Foods
Same address
Tel: 071–238 6167

Food Labelling in Scotland:
Department of Agriculture and Fisheries for Scotland
Room 113
Pentland House
Robb's Loan
Edinburgh EH14 1TW
Tel: 031–244 6185

Genetic Counselling
Genetic Counselling clinics are run by most large hospitals. For details of your nearest clinic, ring your Regional or District Health Authority. These clinics advise people whose genetic code may have health implications for them or for their children.

Genetics Forum—consumer group
258 Pentonville Road
London N1 9JY
Tel: 071–278 6578

Green Alliance
49 Wellington Street
London WC2
Tel: 071–836 0341

Health and Safety Executive
Baynards House
1 Chepstow Place
Westbourne Grove
London W2 4TF
Tel: 071–243 6000

Institute of Medical Ethics
1 Doune Street
Edinburgh EH3 6DY

LINK Agro-Food Quality
Chief Scientist's Group
Ministry of Agriculture, Fisheries and Food
Nobel House
17 Smith Square
London SW1P 3JR
Tel: 071–238 5544

Medical Research Council
20 Park Crescent
London W1N 4AL
Tel: 071–636 5422

*The MRC funded £40 million into genetic engineering research in
1989/90.*

Medicines Control Agency
Department of Health
1 Nine Elms Lane
Vauxhall
London SW8 5NQ

Ministry of Agriculture, Fisheries and Food
Whitehall Place
London SW1
Tel: 071–270 3000

National Consumer Council
20 Grosvenor Gardens
London SW1W OBD
Tel: 071–730 3469

Parents for Safe Food
102 Gloucester Place
London W1
Tel: 071–935 2099

Patent Office
Room 114
State Office
66–71 High Holborn
London WC1R 4TP
Tel: 071–829 6303

Pesticides Safety Division
Ministry of Agriculture, Fisheries and Food
Harpenden Laboratory
Hatching Green
Harpenden
Herts AL5 2BD
Tel: 05827 5241 (ext. 2253)

Plant Breeders' Rights
Plant Variety Rights Office
White House Lane
Huntingdon Road
Cambridge CB3 OLF
Tel: 0223 342372

Scottish Home and Health Department
Chief Scientist's Office
Room 207
St Andrew's House
Waterloo Place
Edinburgh EH1 3DE
Tel: 031–556 8400 (ext. 2739)

Soil Association
86 Colston St
Bristol B51 5BB
Tel: 0272 290661

World Wildlife Fund
Panda House
Weyside Park
Godalming
Surrey
Tel: 0483 426444

APPENDIX 4
Glossary of Terms

AIDS: Acquired Immune Deficiency Syndrome—a cluster of medical problems arising from the destructive effects of the virus HIV.

Amino acid: A chemical structure which forms the basic building block of proteins. Twenty different amino acids occur naturally, and each protein has different characteristics depending on how the amino acids are strung together. The strings are called polypeptide chains, and tend to bunch and coil up to produce complex shapes essential for biological function. The order in which amino acids are built is decided by genes.

Base: The name for nucleotides, the building blocks of DNA. The four bases are cytosine, adenine, thymine and guanine. When arranged in order along a chain they form a unique biological language with a four-letter alphabet (C A T and G). Each group of three bases on a gene corresponds to one type of amino acid.

Biotechnology: The use of biological organisms, systems or processes in manufacturing or research.

Blastomere: Ball of dividing cells at very early stage after fertilisation. At this stage lack of determination means that cells separated from the rest will develop into perfect clones of the original.

Body (somatic) cell: A cell used by the body in life, but not giving rise to sperm, eggs, pollen or ova. If body cells are genetically altered, the alterations are not passed on to subsequent generations—unlike germ cells (qv).

Cell: The smallest living component of all organisms, usually with the capacity to grow and divide. Almost all cells contain genes contained in the cell nucleus.

Chimerism: An organism composed of cells derived from fertilised eggs of the same or different species.

Chromosomes: Strings of genes contained in the nucleus of the cell. Humans have twenty-two pairs of chromosomes, together with two sex chromosomes.

Clone: A group of genetically identical cells or organisms derived from a common ancestor.

Congenital: A condition present at the moment of birth.

Differentiation: The process of specialisation allowing cells to use only part of their genetic information.

DNA: Deoxyribose Nucleic Acid is the substance produced when strings of bases are built together to encode genetic information.

Dominant: A trait or characteristic of a gene which is more active than another with which it is paired.

Enzyme: A protein that acts like a biological machine joining structures together, assembling structures, or tearing them apart.

Gamete:
Sperm or egg—cells containing half a complete set of genes, and used in the process of reproduction. The equivalent in plants are pollen or ova called sporangia.

Gene:
A string of bases which contain instructions for building a particular polypeptide, usually to form a protein.

Gene expression:
The formation in the cell of proteins built using the instructions from that gene.

Gene pool:
A complete set of all the genes, including variants, in a population.

Gene therapy:
An attempt by doctors to reprogram cells in the body to cure disease, or reduce symptoms.

Genetic disease:
A medical problem resulting from an abnormal gene.

Genetic engineering:
Human intervention designed to produce artificial changes in genetic code of organisms that could not be produced as quickly (if at all) by the normal techniques of interbreeding.

Genome:
The entire genetic encyclopedia of a species, usually used of the human.

Germ line:
Germ line cells are cells which are specialised in the body to produce sperm or eggs, or pollen and ova. Reprogramming germ line cells has drastic consequences because offspring will inherit the changes, as will subsequent generations, even though those changes may not be expressed.

HIV:
Human Immunodeficiency Virus causing AIDS.

Interbreeding:
The process of mating one animal with another, or of fertilising one plant with pollen from another, to produce a new favourable mix of genes in a new breed.

In vitro:
In the laboratory flask or test-tube.

In vivo:
In a living organism.

Meiosis: When a germ line cell divides into two cells, each of which has only half a set of genes, as sperm or eggs, pollen or ova.

Mitosis: When a cell divides producing two identical cells, each of which contains a full chromosome set.

Mutation: When genetic code is altered.

Nucleotide: See Base.

Nucleus: A bag of protein inside the cell containing genes arranged in chromosomes.

Plasmid: A protein bag produced by bacteria, containing a loop of DNA which can be passed to other bacteria, effectively reprogramming them. Plasmids are naturally occurring and are similar to viruses in their effect.

Polypeptide: A string of amino acids as part of a protein.

Protein: The structure of life. Large complicated arrangements of polypeptide chains with enormously varied physical characteristics, eg human hair, cornea of the eye, muscle, skin.

Recessive: A trait or characteristic of a gene which is never expressed or activated in the cell unless both genes in the pair of chromosomes coding for the activity are saying the same thing. A recessive trait may not be apparent therefore unless inherited from both parents.

Recombinant DNA: DNA made by joining (recombining) fragments of DNA together by genetic engineering techniques.

Replication: The process by which DNA is duplicated when cells divide.

Retrovirus: A type of virus which uses RNA to write DNA in the cell nucleus rather than the other way round. The best known retrovirus is HIV causing AIDS.

Ribosome: A protein building factory inside the cell, using RNA to determine the sequence of amino acids.

RNA: Ribonucleic acid is a similar structure to DNA and is made by copying DNA in the nucleus. RNA then moves out of the nucleus and is used by ribosomes to provide instructions for building proteins.

Somatic cell: See Body cell.

Stem cell: A moderately differentiated cell that sits in an organ (eg bone marrow) producing other cells which then become more specialised.

Trait: A characteristic programmed by a particular gene or group of genes, eg hair colour.

Virus: An infectious agent— complex protein bag containing a small amount of genetic material (RNA or DNA) and enzymes to use the code to reprogram chromosomes inside the nuclei of cells. Many viruses cause disease, but others can be used as carriers of new genes into cells as part of genetic experiments.

Zygote: Cell formed by the union of two gametes, eg a sperm and an egg uniting to form a fertilised egg poised to start dividing to form a whole human being.

APPENDIX 5
Notes

1. 'Such stuff as genes are made on', *The Independent* (23 March 1992). In fact nearly all the major gene defects in humans have now been identified and the rate of discovery is tailing off.
2. 'Why Gareth's dead head will be one of the frozen few', *The Independent* (26 March 1990).
3. 'Genetic scientists dissect the anatomy of human intelligence', *The Independent* (11 April 1992).
4. 'Prospects for gene replacement therapy', *Birth Defects*; 1987 (23) 3; pp 297–321.
5. Thomas Savery—first steam water pump for miners in 1698. James Watt patented his famous engine in 1769 (*Encyclopaedia Britannica*).
6. Uganda government figures, 1992.
7. *Encyclopaedia Britannica*, 1979.
8. Vines and Rees, *Plant and Animal Biology* (Pitman, 1971).
9. 'Molecular pathology of haemophilia', *Q.J.Med*; 1987 (June); 63 (242); pp 473–91.
10. 'Genetic engineering of Factor 8', *Nature*; 1989 (Nov 9); 342 (6246); pp 207–8.
11. 'Artificial chromosomes', *Scientific American*; 1987 (Nov); 257 (5); pp 62–8.
12. Mature red blood cells have no nucleus and carry no DNA. Sperm and eggs carry only half the total genes needed for life.
13. It is true that I am excluding here, as elsewhere, mature red blood cells which have no nucleus once released into the blood, and sperm or eggs with only 1,500,000,000 bases in them.

14. DNA was first isolated in 1869. The chemical formula for DNA was worked out in 1930, but it was only recognised as genetic in 1950, and the special double helix shape was then worked out in 1953 by Watson and Crick.
15. With the exception of mature red blood cells which contain no nucleus or DNA, and sperm/eggs containing only half a set of chromosomes.
16. It is true that the process of differentiation is far more complex than this and not fully understood.
17. For example: 'Transgenic mice', *Bioessays*; 1987 (Feb); 6 (2); pp73–6.
18. 'Germ line therapy and the clinical ethos of medical genetics', *Theor. Med.*, 1989 (June); 10 (2); pp 151–65.
19. *Nature*; 1992 (Jan 23); 355; p 286.
20. Aldous Huxley, *Brave New World* (1932).
21. 'When is cloning lawful?', *J. In Vitro Fert. Embryo Transf.*; 1987 (Aug); 4 (4); pp 198–204.
22. 'Genetic transformation of animal germ cells by microinjection of the cloned genes into the pronuclei or into the early embryos', *Ontogenez*; 1985 (Nov–Dec); 16 (6); pp 553–67 (Russian). 'The role of transgenic animals in the analysis of various biological aspects of normal and pathological states', *Exp. Cell Res*; 1989 (Aug); 183 (2); pp 257–76.
23. 'Cloning of cow and sheep embryos', *Genome*; 1989 (31) 2; pp 956–62.
24. *ibid*.
25. 'New knowledge and aspects in the use of biotechnology', *2-Gesamte Inn. Med.*, 1986 (May 1); 41 (9); pp 249–55.
26. 'Scientists horrified by giant livestock', *The Sunday Times* (15 March 1992).
27. Personal communication in 1985 from UK university research worker.
28. Z. Harsanyi and R. Hutton, *Genetic Prophecy* (Granada, 1982). There is also some evidence for a genetic influence on the development of sexual orientation, although this appears to be greatly affected also by childhood experience. In 1952 Kallmann carried out a study showing 100% concordance for sexual orientation in twins raised apart. He later revised his figures, but the association remained high. The work was repeated in 1968 by Heston and Shields who also found some concordance. See *Journal Nerv. Ment. Disorders*; F.J. Kallmann (1952): 115, 283 and *Arch. Gen. Psychiat.*; L. Heston and J. Shields (1968): 18, 149. The

message is that many things about us seem to be influenced by a combination of inherited and environmental factors.

29. It is possible that further studies may also show a correlation between faith and genetic code: that something in our genetic makeup can make spiritual awareness more or less likely. For those who emphasise God's call of his elect, rather than total free will, this would come as no great surprise. Perhaps just as the Bible picture is of a God who calls, and people who choose, so the gene/environment/will picture is also mixed. Most Christians would accept that environmental influence—eg family—plays a big part in whether or not someone becomes a believer. The biggest environmental influence is the witness of other believers.

30. Amy and Elizabeth: the second child was born in 1987, eighteen months after the first, to the same parents. Source: D. Winter, *Choose Life* (Marshall Pickering, 1988).

31. 'Fetal tissue transplantation, bone marrow transplantation and prospective gene therapy in severe immunodeficiencies and enzyme deficiencies', *Thymus*; 1987; 10 (1–2); pp 75–87.

32. 'Kidney shortage fuels debate on medical ethics', *The Independent* (5 April 1990).

33. 'Doctors ignored previous warning on transplants', *The Independent* (5 April 1990).

34. 'Doctors ignored previous warning on transplants', *The Independent* (5 April 1990). In fact the quote is not quite fair to the full situation since those with kidney failure can almost always be maintained on dialysis, albeit with some complications to health. This is quite unlike the situation of someone with severe deterioration of the heart.

35. 'Kidney shortage fuels debate on medical ethics', *The Independent* (5 April 1990).

36. This is a controversial statement. The reason offered is that many kidney problems tend to affect both kidneys at once, so having a 'spare' is much less of an advantage than you might think. Congenital absence of one kidney is fairly common, and usually undiscovered until well into adult life—if ever—often as a result of a routine investigation.

37. 'Kidney shortage fuels debate on medical ethics', *The Independent* (5 April 1990).

38. Suggestion made by Robert Shapiro in *The Human Blueprint* (Cassell, 1992).

39. 'Doctors ignored previous warning on transplants', *The Independent* (5 April 1990).

40. 'Genetic engineering in transplant research', *Transplant Proc.*; 1987 (Feb 19); pp 36–9.
41. 'Mice as people', *The Independent* magazine (20 April 1991), pp 26–30.
42. 'Biohazard': 110-page document produced by National Anti-vivisection Society in London in 1987. Quotes over 1,000 scientific papers relating to deliberate transmission of lethal viruses from species to species in US primate centres in the 1960s and 1970s.
43. 'Fetal tissue transplantation, bone marrow transplantation and prospective gene therapy in severe immunodeficiencies and enzyme deficiencies', *Thymus*; 1987; 10 (1–2); pp 75–87.
44. 'A century of neurotransplantation in animals', *Neurochirurgie*; 1990 (36) 2; pp 71–95.
45. *ibid.*
46. Commercial surrogacy is illegal in the UK under the Surrogacy Arrangement Act 1985 and the Human Fertilisation and Embryology Act 1990.
47. 'BMA clears the way for surrogate motherhood', *The Independent* (March 1990) quoting British Medical Association paper entitled 'Surrogacy Report'. Options discussed are: a surrogate mother giving her services free, or being paid expenses, or a substantial fee; a surrogate mother 'providing' her own egg; a surrogate mother receiving an embryo; the egg, sperm, or embryo coming from a donor and not the commissioning man or woman; a surrogate who is a close personal friend or relation of the commissioning couple.
48. I have the press cutting before me describing this case. *The Independent* (1990, exact date lost).
49. Quote from D. Winter, *Choose Life* (Marshall Pickering, 1988), p112. Attributed by the author to David Woollam, a Cambridge embryologist.
50. US Supreme Court judgement 1980: Diamond v Chakrabarty.
51. 'Claims on tissue plasminogen activator', *Nature*; 1989 (Jan 26); 337 (6205); pp 317–8.
52. 'Whose genes are they anyway?', *The Independent* (6 June 1991), p19. Although the oncomouse was approved by the European Patent Office in 1991, pending an appeal in 1993, a similar application for a hairless mouse has been declined on ethical grounds because research into hair growth and human baldness would be at the expense of mice developing cancers: 'Hairless mouse falls victim to tougher regime', *The Independent* (30 November 1992). There is also the need to prove a genetic 'invention'.

53. 'Patent plan for breasts set to stir passions', *The Independent* (19 February 1992).

54. 'Life forms protectable as subjects of US patents—microbes to animals', *Applied Biochem. Biotechnology*; 1987 (Sep–Dec); 16 (6); pp 79–93.

55. *ibid.*

56. 'Patent plan for breasts set to stir passions', *The Independent* (19 February 1992).

57. 'Gene Therapy Panel: NIH merger to shorten review', *Nature*; 1992 (Feb 20); p664. The streamlining of review procedures will make approval of federal-funded gene experiments *easier* to obtain.

58. 'Congress to weigh animal patents', *Science*; 1987; 236 (4805); p 1058. 'Patent office puts Genentech out in front', *Nature* 1987 (Nov 12–18); 330 (6144); p97.

59. 'Groups to fight the new genetic law', *The Independent* (6 June 1991), p 1.

60. 'Patents for new life forms', Dr Susan Mayor, *Third Way* (Feb 1992), pp 23–5.

61. 'German moratorium urged', *Science*; 1987 (Feb 13); 235 (4790); p 741.

62. 'Australian innovation covered by US patent', *Nature*; 1989 (Oct 12); 341 (6242); p 473.

63. 'Biotechnology patents: Dupont battles with Cetus', *Nature*; 1989 (Nov 2); 342 (6245); p 9.

64. Example: 'EC announces bovine hormone moratorium', *Nature*; 1989 (Sep 28); 341 (6240); p 274.

65. 'Greens losing gene battle', *Nature*; 1990 (Aug 16); 346 (6285); p 601.

66. 'Earning the right to own a species', *The Independent* (16 April 1990).

67. 'New genes for old', *Scientific American*; 1988 (Feb); 258 (2); pp 32, 34.

68. 'The polymerase chain reaction: an improved method for the analysis of nucleic acids', *Hum. Genet.*; 1989 (Aug); 83 (1); pp 1–15.

69. 'Plasmids in the environment', *Schrifteur-ver-Wasser-Boden-Lufthyg*; 1988 (78); pp 197–224.

70. 'Plasmids: properties and use in genetic engineering', *Genetika*; 1986 (Aug); 22 (8); pp 2042–7 (Russian).

71. 'Gene escape model: transfer of heavy metal resistance genes from E. coli', *App. Environ. Microbiol.*; 1990 (Aug); 56 (8); pp 2471–9.

72. 'Problems and potential for in situ treatment of environmental pollutants by engineered micro-organisms', *Microbiol. Sci*; 1987 (Feb); 4 (2); pp 59–63.

73. 'Biotechnological treatment of industrial waste water', *Microbiol. Sci*; 1988 (June); 5 (6); pp 186–90.

74. Of course there is no telling what else these microbes might eat when they have finished with the cars, although we can have a good guess because the metabolic capabilities of these genetically modified organisms will be known.

75. 'Invasion by viruses raises gene safety fear', *The Independent* (29 May 1991).

76. 'A high efficiency method for site-directed mutagenesis with any plasmid', *Gene*; 1989 (Dec 7); 84 (1); pp 153–7. Average yield of mutants was 60% with simple and rapid techniques.

77. 'Monomeric Insulins obtained by protein engineering and their medical implications', *Nature*; 1988 (June 16); 333 (6179); pp 679–82. However, the insulin story has suffered a slight setback with a number of diabetics seeking legal action against suppliers of the new insulin because they claim it can produce sudden falls in blood sugar, causing loss of consciousness and coma. Many doctors and the manufacturers remain uncertain whether the cause is the new insulin: 'Diabetics poised to sue over insulin switch', *The Independent* (11 June 1991).

78. 'Saccharomyces expressing hepatitis B surface antigen', *Postgrad. Med. Journal*; 1987 (63 Sup 2); 738; pp 65–70.

79. 'Laboratory bench to production scale', *Dev. Biol. Stand*; 1987; 67 (3); pp 201–6.

80. 'Gene transfer into human leukaemia cell lines by electroporation: experience with exponentially decaying and square wave pulse', *Leukaemia Research*; 1991; 15 (6); pp 507–13.

81. 'Electroporation: parameters affecting transfer of DNA into mammalian cells', *Anal. Biochem*; 1987 (Jul); 164 (1); pp 44–52.

82. 'Electroporation for the efficient transfection of mammalian cells with DNA', *Nucleic Acids Research*; 1987 (Feb 11); 15 (3); pp 1311–26. Other techniques also exist: 'Gene replacement by homologous recombination in mammalian cells', *Somat. Cell. Mol. Genetics*; 1987 (July); 13 (4); pp 447–9. Also: 'Electroporation as a technique for producing transgenic fish', *Cell Differ Dev*; 1990 (Feb); 29 (2); pp 123–8.

83. 'Electro-stimulated cell fusion in cell engineering', *Biofizika*; 1987 (Sep–Oct); 32 (5); pp 874–87.

84. 'Stable expression in mammalian cells of transfected genes using

erythrocyte ghost fusion', *Exp. Cell. Res*; 1987 (Nov); 173 (1); pp 218–31. There are many ways of doing this and improvements are being made all the time: 'Targeted gene replacement (of mammal cells)', *Somat. Cell Mol. Genet (US)*; 1990 (Sep); 16 (5); pp 437–41.

85. 'Introduction of foreign genes into tissues of living mice by DNA-coated microprojectiles', *Proceedings of the National Academy of Sciences of the United States of America*; 1991 (Apr); 88 (7); pp 2726–30. Also 'DNA gun on target for gene therapy', *New Scientist*; 1991 (Sep 15); p34. Helium fired gun fires millions of DNA-coated pellets towards animal tissue at 300 metres per second. There is apparently no trauma or skin irritation. Attempts are being made to reduce the size of the microscopic pellets still further to only 0.2 micrometres.

86. 'Putting new muscle into gene therapy', *Research News*; 1991 (Dec 6); pp 1455–6.

87. 'An alternative approach to somatic cell gene therapy', *Proc. Natl. Acad. Sci. USA*; 1988 (May); 85 (9); pp 3150–4.

88. 'Production methods and safety evaluations of cytokines', *Dev. Biol. Stand*; 1988 (69); pp 193–7.

89. 'Gene replacement and expression of foreign DNA in myco-bacteria', *Journal of Bacteriology*; 1990 (Feb); 172 (2); pp 519–24.

90. 'Expression of a multidrug resistance—adenosine deaminase fusion gene', *Journal of Biol. Chem.*; 1989 (May 5); 264 (13); pp 7418–24.

91. 'Regulation of Insulin-gene expression. Implications for gene therapy', *N. Engl. J. Med*; 1987 (Oct 22); 317 (17); pp 1067–76.

92. 'The molecular pathology of haemophilia', *Q. J. Med*; 1987 (Jun); 63 (242); pp 473–91. The chromosome is the X chromosome linked to determination of sex, which is why females are only carriers and only exceptionally develop the disease.

93. 'The human as an experimental system in molecular genetics', *Science*; 1988 (Jun 10); 240 (4858); pp 1483–8.

94. 'Discovery of gene could aid mental handicap screening', *The Independent* (1 June 1991).

95. *The Independent* (26 February 1991).

96. 'Science for love or money?' *The Independent* (17 April 1992). For further discussion of the conflicts of interest that can arise see Chapter 9.

97. 'The truth about human genome research', letter, *The Independent* (3 March 1991).

98. 'Aid for DNA research', *New Scientist* (15 Feb), p15.

99. *The Independent* (April 1991—exact date uncertain).

100. 'Discovery of the gene defect in cystic fibrosis: implications for diagnosis and treatment', *Clin. Pharm (US)*; 1990 (Sep); 9 (9); pp 716–7.

101. 'Who owns the human genome?', *Science*; 1987 (Jul 24); 237 (4813); pp 358–61

102. *The Times* (9 June 1992): researchers from the US National Institute of Health and the UK Medical Research Council. Application refused (September 1992) but appeal has been lodged. *New Scientist* (10 October 1992), p 9.

103. 'Ethical issues in human genome research', *FASEB J*; 1991; 5 (1); pp 55–60.

104. 'Biotechnology and the medicine of the future', *JAMA*; 1988 (Mar 23); 259 (12); pp 1837–44.

105. 'The parallel path to understanding genes', *The Independent* (26 March 1990).

106. 'General approach to the engineering of synthetic DNA', *Bioorg-Khim*; 1985 (Nov); 11 (11); pp 1533–46.

107. The Science Museum in West Kensington is well worth a visit. There is an excellent genetic engineering exhibition on the second floor with three-dimensional molecules of DNA and virus particles as well as some very clear displays on monoclonal antibody production and reading/writing DNA. Admission is free from 4.30–6.00pm Monday to Sunday.

108. 'Clone 3: plasmid drawing and clone management software program for microcomputers', *Biotechniques*; 1990 (Jun); 8 (6); pp 690–3.

109. 'Plasmid optimised for protein design projects', *Gene (Netherlands)*; 1990 (Sep 28); 94 (1); pp 1–7.

110. 'DNA amplification by the polymerase chain reaction', *Anal. Chem*; 1990 (Jul); 62 (13); pp 1202–14.

111. 'Save a bug for technology', *New Scientist* (1 August 1992).

112. 'DNA amplification by the polymerase chain reaction', *Anal. Chem*; 1990 (Jul); 62 (13); pp 1202–14.

113. *ibid*.

114. 'Mendelian inheritance in man', Professor Victor McKusick (Johns Hopkins University USA, 1990).

115. 'Down on the pharm. Animal developers seeking better beasts breed controversy', *Scientific American*; 1990 (Aug); 263 (2); pp 102–3.

116. *ibid*.

117. Quote from *Pacific News Service* (January 1978).

118. 'The human as an experimental system in molecular genetics', *Science*; 1988 (Jun 10); 240 (4858); pp 1483–8.

119. 'Retrovirus vectors for mammalian engineering', *Microbiol. Sci*; 1984 (Nov); 1 (8); p 210.
120. 'Identification in transgenic animals of the Drosophila sequences required for embryonic dorsal pattern formation', *Genes Dev*; 1987 (Aug); 1 (6); pp 615–25.
121. 'The Frankenstein thing: the moral impact of genetic engineering of agricultural animals on society and future science', *Basic Life Sci*; 1986 (37); pp 285–97.
122. 'Transgenic livestock', *J. Reprod. Fertil. Suppl*; 1987; 34 (1–4); pp 237–50.
123. '"Artificial" chromosomes', *Naturwissenschaffen*; 1987 (Feb); 74 (2); pp 78–85 (German).
124. 'The Frankenstein thing: the moral impact of genetic engineering of agricultural animals on society and future science', *Basic Life Sci*; 1986 (37); pp 285–97.
125. 'Man-made yeast raises temperatures', *The Independent* (19 March 1990)—senior officials and committee members were said to be very unhappy about the way the decision was handled by the Ministry of Agriculture, Fisheries and Food. The *New Scientist* magazine condemned the government's 'grave mistake in its handling of access to information on the release of organisms whose genetic blueprints have been altered. No information on the yeast, or even that anybody had applied for it to be approved, was made public before the product received the go-ahead.' The new yeast produces carbon dioxide faster, causing bread to rise more quickly.
126. 'Life forms protectable as subjects of US patents—microbes to animals', *Applied Biochem. Biotechnol*; 1987 (Sep-Dec); 16 (6); pp 79–93.
127. 'Advances in gene engineering of microorganisms', *Genetika*; 1987 (Oct); 23 (10); pp 1741–8 (Russian).
128. 'Agrobacterium in plant disease, biological disease control and plant genetic engineering', *Sci. Prog*; 1990; 74 (293 pt 1); pp 1–13.
129. *The Independent* (17 June 1992).
130. *Checkout* (Channel 4) briefing paper on Genetic Engineering 1990. Copies can be obtained from the Genetics Forum.
131. BBC2 television documentary April 1991.
132. 'Spiked spuds keep beetles at bay', *New Scientist* (22 Aug 1992), p 19.
133. 'Safety testing of Novel food products created by biotechnology and genetic manipulation', *Biotechnol. Genet. Eng. Rev*; 1987; 5 (5); pp 369–95.

134. 'Genetic engineering of plants for virus resistance', *Arch. Virol*; 1990; 115 (1–2); pp 1–21.
135. 'Increased insecticidal effect by a recombinant baculovirus carrying a synthetic hormone gene', *Biochem. Biophys. Res. Commun*; 1989 (Dec 29); 165 (3); pp 1177–83.
136. 'Construction of genetically engineered baculovirus insecticides', *J. Gen. Virol*; 1990 (Jun); 71 (pt 7); pp 1535–44.
137. 'Scorpion insecticide may help protect crops', *The Independent* (4 July 1991). Research by the Institute of Virology and Experimental Microbiology in Oxford.
138. *The Independent* (23 July 1992).
139. 'Genetic engineers aim for the apple of their eye', *The Independent* (16 January 1991).
140. 'Patents for new life forms', *Third Way* (Feb 1992), pp 23–25. Also 'Designer starch boost for industry' *Daily Telegraph* (7 December 1992).
141. 'Genetic engineering of . . . chicken growth hormone', *Mol. Biol (Mosk)*; 1987 (Nov–Dec); 21 (6); pp 1620–4 (Russian).
142. 'Vectors and genes for improvement of animal strains', *J. Reprod. Fertil. Suppl*; 1990 (41); pp 39–49.
143. 'EC passes hormone for cows', *The Independent* (27 March 1991), p 3.
144. 'Animal husbandry and biotechnology', *Tijdschr Diergeneeskd*; 1987 (Jan 1); 112 (1); pp 9–15 (Dutch).
145. 'EC passes hormone for cows', *The Independent* (27 March 1991).
146. 'BST safety hurdle provides test case for biotechnology', *The Independent* (26 November 1990).
147. *The Independent* (16 June 1992).
148. 'BST safety hurdle provides test case for biotechnology', *The Independent* (26 November 1990).
149. *ibid*.
150. 'New approaches to animal vaccines utilising genetic engineering', *Crit. Rev. Microbiol*; 1988; 15 (3); pp 269–95.
151. 'Embryo sexing of farm animals', *Dev. Biol* (NY 1985); 1986; 4; pp 195–216. Human embryos can also be screened for sex—a technique being used to prevent implantation of male embryos in sex-linked diseases such as Duchenne's Muscular Dystrophy (*Nature* 1990—full ref mislaid).
152. 'Characterisation of transgenic livestock production', *Domest. Anim. Endocrinol*; 1990 (Jan); 7 (1); pp 1–18.
153. 'Animal husbandry and biotechnology', *Tijdschr Diergeneeskd*; 1987 (Jan 1); 112 (1); pp 9–15 (Dutch). Also *New Scientist* (11 November 1992), p 13.

154. 'Will Daisy become a monster?', *The Independent* (29 June 1991), quoting Dr John Webster, Professor of Animal Husbandry at Bristol University.
155. 'Life forms protectable as subjects of US patents—microbes to animals', *Appl. Biochem. Biotechnol*; 1987 (Sep–Dec); 16 (6); pp 79–93.
156. 'Gene transfer into mouse embryos', *Devel. Biol* (NY 1985); 1986; 4; pp 1–36.
157. 'The genetic engineering of production traits in domestic animals', *Experientia*; 1991 (Sep 15); 47 (9); pp 913–22.
158. 'Progress on gene transfer in farm animals', *Vet. Immunol. Immunopathol*; 1987 (Dec); 17 (1–4); pp 303–12.
159. *ibid.*
160. 'The role of transgenic animals in the analysis of various biological aspects of normal and pathological states', *Exp. Cell. Res*; 1989 (Aug); 183 (2); pp 257–76.
161. 'Use of liposomes for the association of foreign genetic material to spermatozoa' (Russian), *Biulleten Eksperimentalnoi Biologii I Meditsiny* (JC: a74); 1991 (Sep); 112 (9); pp 292–3.
162. 'Using embryonic stem cells to introduce mutations into the mouse germ line', *Biology of Reproduction*; 1991 (Feb); 44 (2); pp 238–457.
163. *ibid.*
164. 'Alteration of milk composition using molecular genetics', *Journal of Dairy Science*; 1989 (Oct); 72 (10); pp 2826–33.
165. 'Future developments in the manipulation of growth in farm animals', *Vet. Rec*; 1987 (May 23); 120 (21); pp 495–9.
166. 'Animal production industry in the year 2000', *J. Reprod. Fertil. Suppl*; 1990 (41); pp 199–208.
167. 'Transgenic livestock', *J. Reprod. Fertil. Suppl*; 1987; 34 (1–4); pp 237–50.
168. 'Electroporation as a new technique for producing transgenic fish', *Cell Differ Dev*; 1990 (Feb); 29 (2); pp 123–8.
169. 'Production of transgenic rabbits by microinjection of a gene into fertilised rabbit oocytes', *DTW*; 1987 (Sep); 94 (8); pp 476–8.
170. 'Cloning of sheep and cow embryos', *Genome*; 1989 (31) 2; pp 956–62.
171. 'New animal breeding techniques and their application', *J. Reprod. Fert. Suppl*; 1990 (41); pp 3–14.
172. 'Scientists horrified by giant livestock', *The Sunday Times* (15 March 1992).
173. *ibid.*

174. 'Genetic engineering: modified yeasts fine for food', *Nature*; 1990 (Mar 15); 344 (6263); p186.
175. 'Genetic engineering of ethanol production in Escherichia coli', *Appl. Environmental Microbiology*; 1987 (Oct); 53 (10); pp 2420–5.
176. 'Human gene therapy: possibilities and limitations', *Experiention*; 1987 (Apr 15); 43 (4); pp 375–8. Also 'Genetics and the future of medicine', *Somat. Cell. Mol. Genetics*; 1987 (Jul); 13 (4); pp 485–9.
177. 'Recombinant DNA and Surgery', *Ann. Surg*; 1990 (Aug); 212 (2); pp 178–86. 'Surgeons will need to understand basic DNA research . . . to keep up with the revolution in medical therapies that these techniques will cause.'
178. Figures vary according to centre and study, but a commonly accepted one is one baby lost for every 150 tests.
179. 'Cancer test on foetus at 10 weeks', *The Independent* (24 November 1990)—the woman was treated at University College Hospital in London.
180. *ibid.*
181. 'Faulty gene linked to colon cancer', *The Independent* (16 March 1992). Reported in *Science*. Research by ICI Pharmaceuticals. Only some types of colonic cancer have a genetic basis.
182. 'Gene screening breakthrough on inherited disease', *The Independent* (18 March 1992). Work carried out by Professor Winston at the Hammersmith Hospital (Royal Postgraduate Medical School), in conjunction with the Royal Manchester Children's Hospital. The baby was born on 16 March 1992. Work represented a culmination of five years' research in partnership with a team in Houston, Texas.
183. 'Disfiguring gene found by scientists', *The Independent* (19 February 1991). Most cases of neurofibromatosis are caused by the gene NF1. There is a second, rarer, gene NF2 on a different chromosome (22) which produces bilateral acoustic neuroma (deafness).
184. 'Family link to breast cancer', *The Independent* (19 February 1991).
185. 'Discovery of gene could aid mental handicap screening', *The Independent* (1 June 1991). *Fragile X Syndrome* by Hagerman and Silverman (Johns Hopkins, 1992).
186. 'Gene Therapy', *Nature*; 1992 (Feb 20); 355; p 667—quoting from Thomas McKeown, *The Origins of Human Disease* (Blackwell, 1988). Also 'Purchaser's guidelines to genetic services in the NHS' (Royal College of Physicians, 1991).

187. 'From bench to bedside—the impact of the transfer of new biology to clinical practice', *Clin. Invest. Med*; 1988 (Aug); 11 (4); pp 315–20.

188. Z. Harsanyi and R. Hutton, *Genetic Prophecy* (Granada, 1982). Only for HLA B27 is the association significant at the individual level—the others are statistical associations and therefore not much use.

189. 'Do genes protect?', *New Scientist* (24 Aug 1991).

190. 'The good news—and the bad—about gene therapy prospects', *Science*; 1987 (Apr 3); 236 (4797); pp 29–30.

191. 'The shape of drugs to come', *BMA News Review*; 1983. Also 'Gene technology and the drugs of tomorrow', *Pharm. Weekly (Sci)*; 1990 (Feb 23); 12 (1); pp 6–10.

192. 'Protein engineering and design', *Philos. Trans. R. Soc. Lond (Biol)*; 1989 (Aug 31); 342 (1224); pp 447–60.

193. 'Redesigning trypsin via genetic engineering', *Journal of Cell Biochemistry*; 1987 (Mar); 33 (3); pp 199–211.

194. 'Genetically engineered drugs: toxicology with a difference', *Prog. Clin. Biol. Res*; 1987; 235 (9); pp 161–7.

195. 'Human EGF produced by genetic engineering', *Biochem. Biophys. Res. Commun*; 1989 (Sep 15); 163 (2); pp 1100–6.

196. 'Implantation of fibroblasts transfected with human granulocyte colony stimulating factor DNA', *Blood*; 1989 (Sep); 74 (4); pp 1274–80.

197. 'Periplasmic secretion of human growth hormone by Escherichia coli', *Biochem Soc. Trans*; 1989 (Apr); 17 (2); pp 335–7.

198. 'Characterisation of crystals of genetically engineered human manganese superoxide dismutase', *Journal of Mol. Biol*; 1989 (Apr 20); 206 (4); pp 787–8.

199. 'Claims on tissue plasminogen activator', *Nature*; 1989 (Jan 26); 337 (6205); pp 317–8.

200. 'Approaches to gene therapy in disorders of purine metabolism', *Rheum. Dis. Clin. North Am*; 1988 (Aug); 14 (2); pp 459–77.

201. *ibid.*

202. *ibid.*

203. 'Monomeric Insulins obtained by protein engineering and their medical implications', *Nature*; 1988 (June 16); 333 (6174); pp 679–82.

204. 'Human H-chain ferritins—expression in E. coli', *Febs—Lett*; 1988 (Jul 4); 234 (1); pp 61–4.

205. 'Stabilising basic fibroblast growth factor using protein engineering', *Biochem. Biophys. Res. Commun*; 1988 (Mar 15); 151 (2); pp 701–8.

206. 'Human calmodulin expression in E. coli', *Protein Eng*; 1988 (Oct); 2 (4); pp 307–11.
207. 'Genetic engineering of Factor 8', *Nature*; 1989 (Nov 9); 342 (6246); pp 207–8.
208. 'E. coli in biotechnology', *Wein. Med. Wochenschr*; 1986 (Apr 30); 136 (7–8); pp 158–62 (German).
209. 'Gene engineered somatogen', *Antibiot. Med. Biotekhnol*; 1986 (Nov); 31 (11); pp 841–5.
210. 'Court blocks German biotech plant', *Science*; 1989 (Nov 17); 246 (4932); p 881.
211. BBC2 television documentary (April 1991).
212. 'Gene replacement and expression of foreign DNA in mycobacteria', *Journal of Bacteriology*; 1990 (Feb); 172 (2); pp 519–24.
213. 'Human cell models for genetic engineering', *Mod. Prog. Technol*; 1989 (15) 1–2; pp 83–100.
214. 'Human adenosine deaminase from insect larvae', *Proc. Natl. Acad. Sci. USA*; 1990 (Apr); 87 (7); pp 2760–4.
215. 'Stimulation and inhibition of the growth of mice carrying the human growth hormone gene', *Bink. Eksp. Biol. Med*; 1986 (Sep); 102 (9); pp 339–42 (Russian).
216. 'Gene genies', *Brit. J. of Pharm. Pract*; 1990 (Aug); p 267.
217. *ibid.*
218. 'Present status of recombinant clotting factors', *Haemophilia Society Bulletin*; 1991 (Feb); pp 6–7.
219. *ibid.*
220. 'Blood substitute could end world shortage', *The Independent* (19 March 1992). Quoting from research paper in *Nature* of the same date.
221. 'Impact of genetic engineering on the commercial production of antibiotics by streptomyces and related bacteria', *Appl. Biochem. Biotechnol*; 1987 (Sep–Dec); 16 (6); pp 169–90.
222. 'Antibiotics: opportunities for genetic engineers', *Philos. Trans. R. Soc. Lond. (Biol)*; 1989 (Aug 31); 324 (1224); pp 549–62.
223. 'Genetically engineered monoclonal antibodies', *Br. J. Rheumatol*; 1991; 30 Supp 2; pp 36–9.
224. 'Strategies for controlling cancer through genetics', *Cancer Res*; 1987 (Dec 15); 47 (24 pt 1); pp 6814–7.
225. 'Genetically engineered antibody molecules: new tools for cancer therapy', *Cancer Invest*; 1988; 6 (2); pp 185–92. Also 'The magic bullet that burst the bubble', *New Statesman* (September 1992), p 31.
226. 'Engineering monoclonal antibodies', *Nature*; 1989 (Nov 2); 342 (6245); pp 99–100.

227. 'Genetically engineered antibody molecules and their application', *Ann. NY. Acad. Science*; 1987; 507 (10); pp 187–98.

228. 'Genetically engineered antibodies', *Hosp. Pract. Off*; 1989 (Oct); 24 (10); pp 65–9, 77–80.

229. 'Potential risks of tumour virus subgenomes in the production of biologicals', *Dev. Biol. Stand*; 1987; 68 (2–3); pp 51–62.

230. 'Risk of neoplastic transformation from cellular DNA: calculations using an oncogene mode', *Dev. Biol. Stand*; 1987; 68 (2–3); pp 43–9.

231. 'Use of monoclonal antibodies in the treatment of cancer of the pancreas: towards new progress', *Bull. Cancer*; 1990 (77) 3; pp 283–8.

232. 'Antibody engineering', *Philos. Trans. R. Soc. Lond (Biol)*; 1989 (Aug 31); 3774 (47); pp 537–46.

233. 'Antibody engineering and perspectives in therapy', *Biochemie*; 1990 (Sep); 72 (9); pp 639–51.

234. 'Genetically engineered antibodies', *Clinical Chem*; 1989 (Sep); 35 (9); pp 1849–53.

235. 'Seeding of intravascular stents with genetically engineered endothelial cells', *Circulation*; 1989 (Nov); 80 (5); pp 1347–53.

236. 'Introduction of vascular smooth muscle cells expressing recombinant genes in vivo', *Circulation*; 1991; 83 (2); pp 578–83.

237. 'New technology of vaccine production', *Nippon Rinsho*; 1987 (Oct); 45 (10); pp 2333–41 (Japanese).

238. 'Genetic engineering applied to the development of vaccines', *Philos. Trans. R. Soc. Lond (Biol)*; 1989 (Aug 31); 324 (1224); pp 461–76.

239. 'The third generation vaccines', *Padiatirc-Padol*; 1986; 21 (2); pp 197–204.

240. Product name: Engerix B. Vaccine contains twenty micrograms of hepatitis B surface antigen protein, costing £30 per course of three injections. Product sheet: Smith Kline and Trench Laboratories (9.1.91).

241. 'Immunisation against infectious disease' (Her Majesty's Stationery Office (HMSO): London, 1990).

242. 'Engineering bacterial toxins for the development of a new vaccine against whooping cough', *Pharmacol. Res*; 1989 (Nov–Dec); 21 Suppl 2; pp 19–25.

243. 'Recombination in vivo of pseudorabies vaccine strains to produce new virus strains', *Vaccine*; 1990 (Jun); 8 (3); pp 286–8.

244. 'Immunisation against malaria: present knowledge', *Med. Trop (Mars)*; 1990 (Jan–Mar); 50 (1); pp 137–41.

245. 'Gene replacement in parasitic protozoa', *Nature*; 1990 (Nov 8); 348 (6297); pp 171–5.

246. 'Construction of a bivalent oral vaccine for prevention of typhoid fever and cholera diarrhoea', *Sci.China*; 1990 (Jan); 33 (1); pp 44–9.

247. See Note 270.

248. 'Somatic gene therapy for human disease: background and prospects', *Journal of Paediatrics*; 1987 (Feb); 110 (2); pp 167–74.

249. 'Gene success may aid fight against inherited diseases', *The Independent* (6 February 1992). Work by Dr Keith Johnson at Charing Cross Hospital, London.

250. 'The new way to put on genes', *The Independent* (April 1991).

251. 'Gene research offers hope on muscle-wasting disease', *The Independent* (20 March 1992). Work quoted is that of Dr Kay Davies at the Institute of Molecular Medicine in Oxford.

252. *ibid.*

253. 'Future developments in phenylketonuria', *Enzyme*; 1987; 38 (14); pp 296–301.

254. 'Prospects for correction of thalassemia by genetic engineering', *Prog. Clin. Biol. Res*; 1989; 309; pp 141–59.

255. 'Majority of mice show long term expression of a human beta-globin gene after retrovirus transfer into haematopoietic stem cells', *Mol. Cell. Biol*; 1989 (Apr); 9 (4); pp 1476–34.

256. 'Psychiatry, molecular genetics and ethics: the new discoveries and the new issues', *Aust. NZ Journal of Psychiatry*; 1989 (Mar); 73 (1); pp 67–72.

257. 'I would gain nothing by knowing', *The Independent* (24 March 1991). Patient quoted: 'I feel that at the moment there would be nothing to gain by knowing. When I get to 50 I will have [the test] then, for if they bring out drugs for trial and I do have the gene, then they can test the drugs on me.'

258. 'Psychiatry, molecular genetics and ethics: the new discoveries and the new issues', *Aust. NZ Journal of Psychiatry*; 1989 (Mar); 73 (1); pp 67–72.

259. 'Gene transfer into mouse embryos', *Dev. Biol. (NY 1985)*; 1986; 4; pp 1–36.

260. 'Gene transfer into primates and prospects for gene therapy in humans', *Prog. Nucleic Acid Res. Mol. Biol*; 1989 (36); pp 311–22.

261. 'Progress towards human gene therapy', *Science*; 1989 (Jun 16); 244 (4910); pp 1275–81.

262. 'Gene transfer into primates and prospects for gene therapy in

humans', *Prog. Nucleic Acid Res. Mol. Biol*; 1989 (36); pp 311–22.

263. 'Aerosols may soon be used to treat cystic fibrosis', *The Independent* (21 November 1990).

264. 'Gene therapy for CF advances', *Research News* (17 January 1992)—also see *Science* (19 April 1991), pp 374, 431, and *Cell* (10 January 1992).

265. 'Respiratory tract gene transfer. Transplantation of genetically modified T-lymphocytes directly to the respiratory epithelial cell surface', *Journal of Biological Chemistry*; 1991 (Sep); 266 (27); pp 1839–44.

266. 'Gene therapy for CF advances', *Research News* (17 January 1992)—also see *Science* (19 April 1991), pp 374, 431, and *Cell* (10 January 1992).

267. 'Britain blazes an alternative trail for gene therapy', *New Scientist* (15 Feb), p 15; also 'Charity to pay for gene research', *The Independent* (2 February 1992).

268. 'Britain blazes an alternative trail for gene therapy', *New Scientist* (15 Feb), p 15.

269. 'Gene Therapy', *Nature*; 1992 (Feb 20); 355; p 667—quoting from Thomas McKeown, *The Origins of Human Disease* (Blackwell, 1988).

270. 'Such stuff as genes are made on', *The Independent* (23 March 1992)—quoting Sir David Weatherall, Nuffield Professor of Clinical Medicine at the University of Oxford and author of the classic textbook *The New Genetics and Clinical Practice*.

271. 'Lifespan extension of basal cell nevus syndrome fibroblasts by transfection with mouse pro or v-myc genes', *International Journal of Cancer*; 1987 (May 15); 39 (5); pp 649–55.

272. 'Gene therapy may have future role in cancer treatment', *Journal of the American Medical Association (JAMA)*; 1987 (Jan 9); 257 (2); pp 150–1.

273. 'Scientists identify a genetic link in cancers', *The Independent* (23 March 1990).

274. 'Genetic swaps may halt cancer', *The Independent* (18 February 1991).

275. 'Local administration of cells containing an inserted IL-Z gene and producing IL-Z inhibits of human tumours in nu/nu mice', *Immunol. Lett*; 1988 (Dec); 19 (4); pp 279–82.

276. 'Why Gareth's dead head will be one of the frozen few', *The Independent* (26 March 1990). The company name is Alcor. Over a dozen in the UK have already signed up. There are 450 members

in the USA of which thirteen are already in the fridge. See also 'Cold comfort at death's door', *New Scientist* (26 September 1992), pp 36–39.

277. *Encyclopaedia Britannica* (1979)—Aging, Human, Vol 1, p 305.

278. 'Effects of age on body linked to the role of genes', *The Independent* (27 March 1992). Article quotes Tom Kirkwood, ageing expert at the National Institute of Medical Research in London, speaking at a conference organised by the charity Research into Ageing: 'The idea that we age because our genes treat us as disposable may be unwelcome, but the theory is well supported by evidence and it provides an excellent framework in which a huge variety of observations and hypotheses about ageing in animals can be brought together . . . There is nothing to say that the average human lifespan cannot be extended.' See also 'Who wants to live for ever?' *New Scientist* (14 November 1992), p 160.

279. Blood samples from Africa as early as 1960 test positive for HIV: *New Scientist* (22 Jan 1987). One sample dated 1959 was also positive. An AIDS case has been confirmed recently in the UK in a sailor who died in Manchester in 1959: *The Independent* (6 July 1990).

280. World Health Organisation estimates.

281. *ibid*.

282. 'Search for an immune response that counts', *New Scientist* (27 April 1991).

283. 'Putting candidate vaccines through their paces', *New Scientist* (27 April 1991). See also 'AIDS vaccine testing to begin', *The Independent* (30 November 1992) and *New Scientist* (14 November 1992), p 11.

284. 'AIDS vaccines: what chance of a fair trial?', *New Scientist* (27 April 1991); pp 33–35.

285. Papers presented at the Amsterdam world AIDS conference (July 1992). The accelerating effects have been seen in the laboratory, but may not be significant clinically.

286. 'Secretion of virus-like gag particles of HIV-2 from recombinant baculovirus-infected insect cells', *Virology (US)*; 1990 (Dec); 179 (2); pp 874–80.

287. 'AIDS researchers take step towards gene therapy', *New Scientist*; 1991 (June 29); p 18.

288. 'Applying the PDR principle to AIDS', *J. Theor. Biol*; 1988 (Feb 21); 130 (4); pp 469–80.

289. P. Dixon, *The Truth About AIDS* (Kingsway, 1987); revised and

updated 1989. US edition, *The Whole Truth About AIDS* (Thomas Nelson, 1990); revised international edition 1991, also Kingsway.

290. Several methods exist eg, 'Gene transfer into mammalian cells by electroporation', *Tanpakushitsu Kakusan Koso*; 1987 (Jan); 32 (1); pp 10–21 (Japanese).

291. 'Implantation of genetically engineered fibroblasts into mice: implications for gene therapy', *Science*; 1987 (May 8); 236 (4802); pp 714–8. This approach is known technically as 'Transkaryotic implantation'.

292. 'Adult mammalian hepatocyte as target cell for retroviral gene transfer—a model for gene therapy', *Somat. Cell. Mol. Genetics*; 1987 (Jul); 13 (4); pp 423–8.

293. 'Retroviral . . . gene transfer in . . . primates following . . . bone marrow transplantation', *Ann. N.Y. Acad. Sci*; 1987; 511 (8); pp 406–17.

294. 'A genetically engineered cell line that produces empty capsids of BA (human) parvovirus', *Proc. National Acad. Science USA*; 1989 (Oct); 86 (19); pp 7601–5.

295. 'Gene transfer: a potential approach to gene therapy for sickle cell disease', *Ann. N.Y. Acad. Sci*; 1989 (565); pp 37–43.

296. 'Gene transfer to primary normal and malignant human hemopoietic progenitors using recombinant retroviruses', *Blood*; 1987 (Feb); 69 (2); pp 611–7.

297. 'Storm rages as gene therapy makes debut', *Hospital Doctor*; 1990 (Nov 15); p 19.

298. Adenosine deaminase deficiency.

299. 'Gene transplant therapy in girl "achieving success"', *The Independent* (20 February 1991). See also 'A first for British doctors', *The Daily Telegraph* (7 December 1992).

300. 'Stem-cell gene therapy moves towards approval', *Science*; 1992 (Feb 28); 255; p 1072.

301. 'Gene Genies', *B. Journal of Pharm. Pract*; 1990 (Aug); p 267.

302. *ibid.*

303. 'Hazards of genetic engineering', *Nature*; 1987 (Mar 26); 326 (6111); p 326—also 'Stop all further extensions of production using genetic technology', *Sygeplejersken*; 1987 (Sep 2); 87 (36); pp 30–1.

304. 'The use of genetic engineering in veterinary medicine with examples from epidemiology, diagnosis and drug production', *TierarzH Prax*; 1990 (Apr); 18 (2); pp 99–108.

305. 'NATO recommendations for a scientific approach to safety assurance for environmental introductions of genetically engineered

organisms', *Rom. Recomb. DNA Tech. Bull*; 1987 (Dec); 10 (4); pp 115–22—also 'Britain regulates organism release', *Nature*; 1989 (Oct 26); 341 (6244); p 681. Also 'Tight controls urged on the use of genetically altered organisms', *The Independent* (March 1990)—quoting concerns of Lord Lewis of Newnham, Chairman of the Royal Commission on Environmental Pollution. A great number of examples of ecological damage—eg 'Alien weed keeps travelling west', *New Scientist* (17 October 1992), p 8; and 'Alien predators devastate Australian wildlife', *New Scientist* (12 September 1992), p 4.

306. 'Can we guarantee the safety of genetically engineered organisms in the environment?', *Crit. Rev. Biotechnol*; 1988 (8)1; pp 85–97.

307. 'Electroporation as a new technique for producing transgenic fish (rainbow trout)', *Cell Differ. Dev*; 1990 (Feb); 29 (2); pp 123–8.

308. 'Contribution to the discussion on the release of transgenic organisms', *Naturwissenschaffen*; 1991 (May); 78 (5); pp 209–14—also April; 78 (4); pp 154–7, same journal.

309. 'Agrobacterium in plant disease, biological disease control and plant genetic engineering', *Sci. Prog*; 1990; 74 (293 pt 1); pp 1–13.

310. 'Growth of genetically engineered pseudomonas aeroginosa and pseudomonas putida in soil and rhizosphere', *Appl. Environ. Microbiol*; 1989 (Dec); 55 (12); pp 3243–6.

311. 'Domesticated bacteria or Andromeda strains?', *Bioessays*; 1987 (Aug); 7 (2); p 87.

312. 'Model to predict aerial dispersal of bacteria during environmental release', *Appl. Environ. Microbiol*; 1989 (Oct); 55 (10); pp 2641–7.

313. 'Survival of bacteria during aerosolisation', *Appl. Environ. Microbiol*; 1990; 56 (11); pp 3463–7.

314. 'Effect of aerosolisation on subsequent bacterial survival', *Appl. Environ. Microbiol*; 1990 (Nov); 56 (11); pp 3468–72.

315. 'Transport of a genetically engineered pseudomonas fluorosens strain through a soil microcosm', *Appl. Environ. Microbiol*; 1990 (Feb); 56 (2); pp 401–8.

316. 'Small scale field testing of the genetically engineered LacZY marker', *Regul. Toxicol. Pharmacol;* 1990 (Jun); 11 (3); pp 253–61.

317. 'Can we guarantee safety of genetically engineered organisms in the environment?', *Crit. Rev. Biotechnol*; 1988 (8)1; pp 85–97.

318. 'Microcosm for assessing survival of genetically engineered micro-organisms in aquatic environments', *Appl. Environ. Microbiol*; 1990 (Apr); 56 (4); pp 977–83.

319. 'Survival capacity of genetically altered Escherichia coli strains', *Zentralblatt fur Hygiene und Umweltmedizin (JC: ac1)*; 1991 (Sep); 192 (1); pp 1–13.

320. 'Physical and chemical control of released microorganisms at field sites', *Canadian Journal of Microbiology*; 1991 (Sep); 37 (9); pp 708–12.

321. 'Unauthorised release upsets EPA', *Nature*; 1987 (Aug); 328 (6132); p 659—also 'West German release of altered bacteria causes furor', *Nature*; 1987 (Aug); 328 (6131); p 568.

322. 'Evolutionary principles and the regulation of engineered bacteria', *Genome*; 1989; 31 (2); pp 864–9.

323. *ibid.*

324. 'Alteration of the Meno virus through genetic engineering', *Nature*; 1990 (Feb 1); 343 (6257); pp 474–6. Work being applied to development of a vaccine for foot and mouth disease.

325. *The Independent magazine* (20 April 1991), p 30.

326. *ibid.*

327. 'Problems of safety in biotechnology. Products of genetic engineering and regulation of work with them', *Mil. Gen. Mikrobiol. Virusol*; 1987 (Sep); 52 (9); pp 3–10 (Russian).

328. Culture Collection of Algae and Protozoa: 1,700 cultures
International Mycological Institute: 15,000 cultures
National Collection of Food Bacteria: 2,000 cultures
National Collections of Industrial and Marine Bacteria: 3,800 cultures
National Collection of Type Cultures: 17,800 cultures
National Collection of Pathogenic Fungi: 830 cultures
National Collection of Plant Pathogenic Bacteria: 3,000 cultures
National Collection of Yeasts: 2,000 cultures
European Collection of Animal Cell Cultures: 800 cultures

Addresses and telephone numbers listed in *Biotechnology: a plain man's guide to the support and regulations in the UK* (Department of Trade and Industry, ISBN 1–85324–5100).

329. 'Biosafety considerations in industries with production methods based on the use of recombinant DNA', *Scand. J. Work. Environ. Health*; 1990 (16) 2; pp 85–95.

330. 'Production methods and safety evaluation of cytokines', *Devel. Biol. Stand*; 1988 (69); pp 193–7.

331. Extracts from the *Drugs and Therapeutics Bulletin 1991* (June 24); 29, 13, pp 49–50.

332. *ibid.*

333. *Encyclopaedia Britannica* (1979).

334. Press reports, late August 1992, unconfirmed by the Ministry of Defence.

335. *New Scientist* (August 1992).

336. This approach is one currently being developed as a permanent male contraceptive. Abuse of the vaccine, by giving it to children, could easily happen and would be impossible to detect—probably only picked up ten or twenty years later when the children have grown up and are complaining of infertility problems.

337. 'Sex preselection', *British Journal of Hospital Medicine*; 1987 (Feb); 37 (2); pp 149, 151–2, 154–5. Also 'Clinical relevance of sex selection techniques', *Fertil. Steril*; 1989 (Dec); 52 (6); pp 891–905.

338. 'Sex preselection in humans by enrichment of X or Y chromosome bearing spermatozoa', *Andrologia*; 1987 (Mar-Apr); 19 (2); pp 157–60.

339. 'Sex preselection in New York city: who chooses which sex and why?', *Int. J. Fertil*; 1989 (Sep-Oct); 34 (5); pp 353–4.

340. 'Transgenic livestock', *J. Reprod. Fertil. Suppl*; 1987; 34 (14); pp 237–50.

341. 'Biosynthetic hormone and the opinions of paediatricians', *Arch. Fr. Paediatr*; 1986 (Oct); 43 (8); pp 617–20.

342. 'Genetic engineering submission to the British Medical Association', *Journal of the Christian Medical Fellowship* (January 1990), pp 18–22.

343. 'Genetic scientists dissect the anatomy of human intelligence', *The Independent* (11 April 1992).

344. 'Riley-Day Syndrome, brain stimulation and the genetic engineering of a world without pain', *Med. Hypotheses*; 1990 (Mar); 31 (3); pp 201–7.

345. 'Ethical manipulations: an ethical evaluation of the debate surrounding genetic engineering', *Human Gene Therapy*; 1991 (Spring); 2 (1); pp 71–75.

346. Christian Medical Fellowship submission by Dr Caroline Berry, Consultant Clinical Geneticist at Guy's Hospital to the Committee on Ethics of Gene Therapy, Department of Health in March 1990: 'Somatic gene therapy needs to be controlled and monitored with great stringency as with any radically new therapy. Major efforts must be made to explain its nature and scope to patients and the public so that natural but irrational anxieties are allayed.'

347. 'Science for love or money?' *The Independent* (17 April 1992).

348. 'Man-made yeast raises temperatures', *The Independent* (19

March 1990)—senior officials and committee members were said to be very unhappy about the way the decision was handled by the Ministry of Agriculture, Fisheries and Food. The *New Scientist* magazine condemned the government's 'grave mistake in its handling of access to information on the release of organisms whose genetic blueprints have been altered. No information on the yeast, or even that anybody had applied for it to be approved, was made public before the product received the go-ahead'. The new yeast produces carbon dioxide faster, causing bread to rise more quickly. Pure Food Campaign—'Guess what's coming to dinner', *New Scientist* (14 November 1992), pp 13–14.

349. 'Council Directive of 23 April 1990 on the contained use of genetically modified micro-organisms', 90/219/EEC and 'Council Directive of 23 April 1990 on the deliberate release into the environment of genetically modified organisms', 90/220/EEC.

350. *Biotechnology: a plain man's guide to the support and regulations in the UK*, 2nd edition (Crown, 1991, ISBN 1 85324 5100).

351. *ibid.*

352. *ibid.*

353. *ibid.*

354. *ibid.*

355. *Guidelines on the Assessment of Novel Foods and Processes: Report 38 on Health and Social Subjects* (Department of Health HMSO, 1991), £4.25.

356. *The Independent* (23 July 1992).

357. *Guidelines on the Assessment of Novel Foods and Processes: Report 38 on Health and Social Subjects* (Department of Health HMSO, 1991), £4.25.

358. *Biotechnology: a plain man's guide to the support and regulations in the UK*, 2nd edition (Crown, 1991, ISBN 1 85324 5100).

359. *ibid.*

360. *Genetically Modified Organisms: proposed new regulations. A consultation paper* (Health and Safety Commission, Oct 1991).

361. 'Revised gene law "panders to industry"', *New Scientist* (8 August), p 6.

362. 'Sabotage sets back Dutch biotechnology', *New Scientist* (22 August 1992), p 4. The company was Van Der Have.

363. 'Little ventured on Europe's biotechnology', *New Scientist* (11 July 1992).

364. *The Independent* (5 June 1992).

365. *Biotechnology: a plain man's guide to the support and regulations in the UK*, 2nd edition (Crown, 1991, ISBN 1 85324 5100).

366. *ibid*.
367. *ibid*.
368. *ibid*.
369. 'Genetic lamb may be lung cure', *The Independent* (26 April 1990). People with the lung condition called emphysema suffer from breathlessness and wheezing. It is caused by lack of a protein called alpha-1 antitrypsin.
370. Personal communication (April 1992).
371. 'Genetic engineering: new law is overdue', *Nature*; 1989 (Nov 16); 342 (6247); p 218—also 'Genetic engineering; new law needs changes made', *Nature*; 1990 (Jan 25); 343 (6256); p 298.
      'Recombinant DNA regulation. India opts for self control', *Nature*; 1990 (Feb 22); 343 (8260); p 680.
      'West German commission reports on genetic engineering', *Nature*; 1987 (Feb 5–11); 325 (6104); p 474.
372. 'When is cloning lawful?', *J. In Vitro Fert. Embryo Transf*; 1987 (Aug); 4 (A); pp 198–204.
373. 'So God created man in his own image, in the image of God he created him; male and female he created them' (Genesis 1:27).
374. Genesis 1:28.
375. For a Christian, the Bible teaching about life is very important, showing a continuity between pre-natal and post-natal life: 'For you created my inmost being; you knit me together in my mother's womb. I praise you because I am fearfully and wonderfully made; your works are wonderful . . . my frame was not hidden from you when I was made in the secret place. When I was woven together in the depths of the earth, your eyes saw my unformed body. All the days ordained for me were written in your book before one of them came to be' (Psalm 139:13–16).
376. 'Prenatal screening: when and for whom?', *J. Gen. Intern. Med (US)*; 1990 (Sep–Oct); 5; pp 542–6.
377. *ibid*.
378. *ibid*. Most clinics inform expectant mothers of their screening policy on the first visit, but it does not always happen, nor are all patients aware of what tests may mean.
379. *ibid*.
380. *ibid*.
381. Figures vary according to centre and study. A commonly accepted figure is around one baby lost for 150 tests.
382. D. Winter, *Choose Life* (Marshall Pickering, 1988), p 71. New 'triple testing' may increase sensitivity and reduce risk of aborting normal babies in future.

383. 'For God so loved the world that he gave his one and only Son, that whoever believes in him shall not perish but have eternal life' (John 3:16).

384. 'Ethics and medical genetics in the United States: a national survey', *Am. J. Med. Genet*; 1988 (Apr); 29 (A); pp 815–27. Survey contains many other interesting results re ethical attitudes.

385. 'Primary prevention of colorectal cancer—WHO collaborating centre', *Bulletin of WHO*; 1990 (68) 3; pp 377–85.

386. *ibid*.

387. 'Call for UK gene therapy', *Nature*; 1992 (Jan 23); 355; p 286. Also *Lancet* (Jan 25); 339; pp 238–9 and *British Medical Journal* (Jan 25); 304; p 201.

388. 'Gene therapy wins official blessing', *New Scientist* (25 Jan), p18—report of the Committee on the Ethics of Gene Therapy (HMSO, January 1992).

389. 'Danish trade unions oppose ban on screening', *New Scientist* (11 July 1992). It is true that workers with detected genetic problems could choose to be transferred to another part of the factory, but there is no legal means to prevent such data from being improperly used. Trade Unions are opposed to a blanket ban because they want to be able to protect workers. They say it is not screening that is the problem, but who has access to the results.

390. 'Health insurance, HIV testing and genetic risk', *Lancet*; 1991 (Nov 9); 338, p1212.

391. 'Genetic advances will test our moral mettle', *The Independent* (30 April 1990).

392. 'This mouthwash could mean a lot to your children', *The Independent* (20 January 1992). There are in fact 150 gene mutations that can give rise to cystic fibrosis, but the main one accounts for 78% of illness.

393. 'Prenatal screening: when and for whom?', *J. Gen. Intern. Med (US)*; 1990 (Sep–Oct); 5; pp 542–6.

394. 'New Danish law: human life begins at conception', *J. Med. Ethics*; 1988 (Jun); 14 (2); pp 77–8.

395. 'New reproductive technologies in the treatment of human infertility and genetic disease', *Theor. Med*; 1990 (Jun); 11 (2); pp 103–110.

396. 'Limits to genetic intervention in humans: somatic and germ line', *CIBA Found. Symp*; 1990 (149); pp 81–6, 87–92.

397. Gallup Poll commissioned by the Society for the Protection of the Unborn Child (SPUC) (January 1990).

398. 'God blessed them and said to them, "Be fruitful and increase in number; fill the earth and subdue it. Rule over the fish of the sea and the birds of the air and over every living creature that moves on the ground." Then God said, "I give you every seed-bearing plant on the face of the whole earth and every tree that has fruit with seed in it. They will be yours for food"' (Genesis 1:28–29).

399. 'Then God said, "Let us make man in our own image, in our likeness, and let them rule over the fish of the sea and the birds of the air, over the livestock, over all the earth, and over all the creatures that move along the ground"' (Genesis 1:26).

400. In the USA for example: 'Genetic engineering guidelines (up-graded)', *Microbiol. Sci*; 1984; 1 (5); pp 131–2.

401. 'Recombination in vivo of pseudorabies vaccine strains to produce new virus strains', *Vaccine*; 1990 (Jun); 8 (3); pp 286–8.

402. *Nature*; 1992 (Jan 23); 355; p286. Sir Cecil Clothier's independent committee—also see *Daily Telegraph* (16 January 1992).

403. 'Gene therapy: exciting new treatments or sinister eugenics?' Stephanie Lewis, *Care Magazine* (June 1992).

404. See Christian Medical Fellowship submission by Dr Andrew Fergusson to Committee on Ethics of Gene Therapy (April 1992): 'Treatment should be confined to serious genetic disease . . . to prevent any later slide into treating conditions of such a medically trivial nature that they might qualify as "attempts to change human traits associated with disease".'

405. Matthew 6:10.

Index

239

The Truth About Aids
Revised International Edition

by Dr Patrick Dixon

If you care about AIDS—its causes and its effects on people—
this book's for you.

'Excellent and thoroughly readable.'   *Caring Professions Concern*

'Should be available to every GP for his own use and for
lending to those concerned . . . well referenced yet written with
a minimum of technical jargon.'   *The Physician*

'A wealth of research and published material from medical and
popular sources in a detailed and extensively referenced book.'
British Medical Journal

'Probably the best single volume on the whole AIDS issue
available today. I recommend it to pastors and those with care
responsibility as well as others with more general interest.'
Restoration

DR PATRICK DIXON is Founder and Medical Director of AIDS
Care Education and Training (ACET), the church-based charity
which has cared for over 1,000 people ill with HIV/AIDS at
home in the UK. It has a large schools programme, and a
rapidly developing overseas work in Africa, Eastern Europe and
South East Asia.

Kingsway Publications